TORMENTED BY
TECHNOLOGY

TORMENTED BY TECHNOLOGY

The Silent Health Effects of Wireless Electromagnetic Radiation

Susan Jeffrey Busen
with Tom, Will, and Dan Busen

Tormented by Technology

Note to the Reader

The information, ideas, and suggestions presented in this book are not intended as a substitute for professional advice. Before following any suggestions contained in this book, you should consult your personal physician, mental health professional, or someone licensed or certified in the area in which you seek help. You must take complete responsibility for your decision to act based on any suggestions presented herein. Neither the authors nor the publisher shall be liable or responsible for any loss or damage allegedly arising as a consequence of your use or application of any information or suggestions in this book. The only way to know if radiation levels have been reduced or eliminated is to measure the levels with an appropriate meter. The information and suggestions in this book are not intended to diagnose, treat, cure, heal, or prevent any mental or physical condition. They are simply the opinions of the authors. If you think you have a medical condition, consult a licensed medical professional. Consult a qualified electrician for help with grounding or electrical work. Radiation shielding should be done by a qualified professional. Our intention is to educate and inform so you can choose to protect yourself in a way that is best for you. If you are reading the electronic format of this book, please download the book onto your device and read it in airplane mode with the Wi-Fi feature turned off.

Visit www.TormentedByTechnology.com for links and resources.

ISBN-10: 0-9820697-8-2
ISBN-13: 978-0-9820697-8-3
Printed in the United States of America

We dedicate this book to you and your future generations

Also by Susan Jeffrey Busen

Bridging Medicine and Miracles: Essential Truths, Key Practices, and a New Perspective on Health and Healing

Tap into Joy: A Guide to Emotional Freedom Techniques for Kids and Their Parents

Tap into Success: A Guide to Thriving in College Using Emotional Freedom Techniques

Tap into Balance: Your Guide to Awakening the Joy Within Using the GetSet™ Approach

Good Vibes: 48 Tips to Raise Your Vibration—The Secret to Creating a Healthy Lifestyle and Attracting What You Want

EFTタッピングセラピー おとなが子どもにできること
(*Tap into Joy* in Japanese)

Tap into Joy: Energy Clearing for Children of All Ages DVD

Upcoming Books:

Tap into Your Dream: The Secret to Creating the Life You Want

Tap into Hope: A Guide to Helping Children through Grief

Coauthor of *Outside In: A Guided Journal of Self-Reflection and Awakening*

Tap into Balance in Korean

Tap into Joy in Slovenian

Table of Contents

ACKNOWLEDGMENTS

We are deeply grateful to the following:

To our editor, JoAnne Keltner, for your flexibility, expertise, and attention to detail.

To all of our family members and friends who believed in us and supported and encouraged us along the journey.

To the many researchers and scientists and those in the public health sector who are working diligently to warn the public, protect our health, and stop the implementation of technologies until they are proven to be safe. We are impressed by your resolve and willingness to put everything on the line in order to reveal the truth.

To those working to find safer technologies, we thank you for your dedication.

To everyone we interviewed for this book. We are especially appreciative of those who allowed us to share their personal stories. Our candid conversations were enlightening, and your stories are invaluable to us and our readers.

To all who have taken the time to advise us and review this work. We are honored by your passion and generosity.

We admire the courage you have all shown us by standing up for what is right.

SECTION I

When Smart Is Not So Smart

We are living in a sea of radiation. Exposure to radiofrequency radiation levels have increased exponentially over the past two decades. Little is known about the background levels we are exposed to on a daily basis.

We don't know exactly how much radiation is absorbed and how it is distributed in the body. Every source and device puts out different amounts of electromagnetic energy at different frequencies. We are often exposed to numerous sources simultaneously, and never before in history have we been exposed to such levels.

Technology is changing all the time. Every company wants to rush their products to market, beat everyone else, and bypass as much red tape as they can. They do not take the time to conduct true long-term safety studies on each advance and device before it comes out on the market.

As a society, we continually expect our technology to be faster and more convenient, to provide us with instant gratification. Most of us depend on our devices and cannot imagine living without them. The problem is that we use technology largely without any concern of health consequences. A growing body of evidence suggests that our haphazard use of technology can have catastrophic effects on our health. We are experiencing the largest silent epidemic of all time. However, the actions and precautions you take after reading this book will enable you to protect yourself and future generations from technological harm.

Chapter 1

Introduction

Have you ever taken a good look around and simply asked the question, *Why?* Why have cancer rates skyrocketed? Why are so many people, including children, diabetic? Why are young athletes dropping dead on the athletic field? Why are so many people experiencing dementia? Why have autism rates soared? Why are so many people struggling with attention issues, anxiety, and depression? It seems many people need medication just to get by. This is at a time when we are supposedly living longer and experiencing increased quality of life due to medical screenings, diagnostics, and innovative treatments.

When I was growing up, birth defects were rare. Teenage suicide was uncommon. Pediatric cancer was unheard of. People in their thirties did not get dementia. No one in my school was autistic. Attention issues and obsessive behaviors were rare. Now, the typical school nurse's office has become a drug dispensary. Now, there are investment plans for parents to save for the long-term care needs of their children who will never be able to care for themselves. There are pediatric cancer wards at most major hospitals.

Ask anyone who has been in the school system or in the medical profession for thirty years or longer. As a society, our health and well-being has taken a nose-dive. Why are lots of middle-aged people living in nursing homes? Why are there hospitals, medical facilities, cancer centers, and fertility clinics popping up everywhere? Why is this happening? What has changed in the past couple of decades to drive these problems to unprecedented levels? What if wireless radiation were the cause of all of this? What if we were making the biggest mistake of all time by jumping on this technology bandwagon without questioning its effects? What if we are doing this to ourselves in the name of progress? What if industries knew this but were focused on the billions of dollars they would be making as a result of all of these gadgets and upgrades and target marketing abilities? What if there were safer ways to use technology but nobody wanted to take the time to change? What if they knew there was a 20-, 30-, or even 40-year latency period before people would get sick and figure this out? These are questions we must ask ourselves.

Do we want to repeat the mistakes of the past? Think about tobacco, asbestos, thalidomide, glyphosate, and GMOs. There was evidence that these substances were harmful long before we were told about it. In these cases, industry and regulators overlooked the dangers in exchange for profit. When we learn about hazards in our life, we have the choice to eliminate them. We don't have to wait for someone else to protect us. The difference with wireless radiation is that we don't have a choice. Once you realize it is harming you, you can't get away from it unless you completely step out of your life and become reclusive or live as a refugee.

The intention of this book is to educate the lay person on sources of electromagnetic radiation and the harm that can be caused by simple, everyday exposure. It is not meant to be a scientific paper full of citations and complex science. There is plenty of scientific evidence if one merely searches for it online. There are links on our website to wonderful sites compiling numerous scientific studies. For those interested, we urge you to read the published science for yourself and form your own conclusions. There are also many videos where you can watch brilliant scientists and professors presenting their research as it relates to harm caused by electromagnetic radiation and the mechanisms of action which harm human, animal, and plant life.

There are tens of thousands of published studies from around the world that conclude radiofrequency radiation causes biological effects and harm to the body at a cellular level. I have spent well over one thousand hours researching during the past year and a half, have personally read over 500 of these studies, and have watched hundreds of hours of video presentations on the topic. While I won't go into detail on the science, I will provide my thoughts and draw my own conclusions on my findings because you deserve to know.

Scientists know that this research is being conducted and that the findings raise concerns. Scientists read the work of other scientists. There are many scientists, researchers, and public health officials working diligently to try to protect you from this radiation. It is no simple task. They are up against many roadblocks. The problem is twofold. Industry funds most of the studies and does not fund studies that are looking at harm. If a study raises concern, the conclusion generally states that more research is needed to further prove or validate the findings. Funding gets cut off at that point, and it is very difficult to conduct a proper long-term study without funding. The information is filtered before it gets to the media and is never reported to the public. The information that we get from mainstream media is heavily biased to cover up the problems.

There are a number of serious threats that are not talked about in the mainstream. Information is being censored, and if you don't know about it, you can't protect yourself. There is plenty of evidence and research about these threats, but if you don't look for them, you will not find them. This information will not pop up in your newsfeed or show up on your homepage. If you don't know there is a risk, you can't protect yourself and eventually you will suffer the consequences. The price of silence is much too high.

We realize that we alone do not have the credentials or power to change this. We hope to be a voice for those who do not know they are at risk or may be getting harmed. We want to help people to protect themselves at an individual level, from the bottom up, while public health officials work to get regulatory and governmental agencies to protect you from the top down.

We are being bombarded with more wireless radiation than ever before in history. We must take this seriously.

As you read this book, you will be provided with examples of symptoms people experience when they are exposed, with examples of symptoms of overexposure, and with many suggestions for how you can reduce your exposure. Many of the suggestions are a result of searching for solutions to reduce my own exposure after becoming quite ill. Along with sharing my personal story and my son's sharing their stories, we will share some of the stories we have gotten from others who have been affected by the typical exposures that most of us receive regularly while living in this age of increasing technology and the developing smart grid.

It is a widely accepted belief that we are living in an increasingly unhealthy world. Our air, water, soil, and food supply have been accumulating toxins. We must be proactive if we want to stay healthy in today's world. Our intention is to inform you so you can best protect yourself and those you care about in a way that feels right to you.

The degree of seriousness with which you take this information will likely be dependent on your degree of trust, the degree of symptoms you or a loved one are experiencing, your level of fear, and your level of commitment to protect your health and that of future generations.

Chapter 2

Why Sharing This Information Is Important to Us

Before we dive deep into the content of this book, we would like to share where we are coming from, why we are writing this book, and why the topic is important to each of us individually.

We are complex beings. In addition to our physical bodies, we are electromagnetic fields. We have incredible power to co-create our physical existence.

We believe our experience as a family with electrohypersensitivity (EHS) came about to motivate us to learn how to take better care of ourselves amidst this technology and to use our experience to help others. We feel we are at the forefront of contributing to the solution. We need people to join forces. We must stand together and demand safe technology and hold the industries and regulators accountable and liable for the harm they are causing.

Together as a society, we will find solutions. We will drive change. We will hold industries and regulators accountable. In essence, we are the solution. In the meantime, we will warn of the dangers and teach others to protect themselves. We believe the more people who know and care about this issue, the better chance we have of creating change.

Will:

Whether we like it or not, technology has been rapidly woven into the fabric of our daily lives. Technology is now a fundamental element of our culture and it becomes more and more a part of our lives with each passing day. Never in history has innovation experienced such exponential growth over such a short period of time in any other industry. The technological revolution is fascinating to be a part of, especially when seemingly impossible and improbable feats are achievable in record time. Would you have ever in your wildest dreams thought that a store clerk would give you a puzzled look as you hand him or her cash instead of a plastic card or your phone at the *cash* register, or that you would no longer need your landline phone, or that you could summon a car to pick you up at any location within minutes without making a phone call, or that your mail packages could be casually delivered via drone? These sorts of dreams have already become reality, and many other dreams of this magnitude have seemed to transpire practically overnight. This is the world we now live in.

Even millennials are shocked by most of the innovations created each year, though we are quick to adopt and normalize them. You're not the only one constantly asking the question, OMG, what will they think of next? It is nearly inconceivable that the Silent Generation purchased ice blocks for their icebox from a salesman who pulled a cart through the neighborhood alleys and that now smart refrigerators enable us to view the contents of our fridge from our mobile phone while we are at the grocery store. We are so quick to adopt and normalize these technologies that we don't even pause for a moment to question any of it. How can you when the next generation phone or tablet is launching soon and your device will soon be considered outdated? Your technology becomes obsolete before you are able to learn all of its capabilities. It's daunting, not to mention expensive, to keep up with the pace of technology. Consumers continue to demand new and improved products, faster download speeds, and enhanced streaming capabilities and the industry keeps delivering. We have come to expect to be able to stream videos, check emails, and shop from our phone while in the subway or while waiting at red lights.

Where am I going with all of this? Well, I think it's an undisputable fact that the rapid evolution of technology doesn't show signs of slowing down or scaling back anytime soon. This ultimately means we need to put time and energy into learning about how technology affects us and how to consciously manage our exposure to it. We need to pause and ask the questions that we haven't previously bothered to ask. You don't have to be an expert to ask questions and seek answers.

You might feel overwhelmed when you learn just how much you don't know about the science of EMFs and RFs, but that doesn't mean you should simply assume that all of this technology is perfectly safe simply for convenience's sake! Admittedly, I struggle to understand how I can speak into a phone and the other party can hear my voice in real time, and this is technology that has been around since the mid 1800s! It doesn't keep me up at night because it works whether or not I know *how* it works. The phone, along with countless other technologies, is ultimately a convenience for me (and billions of others), so why question it? I think this is the essence of the overarching problem today: people tend not to care much about how something works, what health impact it might have, or the potential non-monetary "cost" of using it as long as they realize the convenience or immediate benefit of using it.

It takes quite a lot of effort to challenge something, particularly things that the mass population accepts. Looking for cracks in the foundation that most others tend to overlook and deciding to dig deeper than others are willing to can result in gaining empowering and liberating knowledge. On one end of the spectrum, there are people who are severely sensitive to wireless radiation and are desperate to understand their condition, while on the other end might be those who are simply curious or attempting to be proactive with their health. For my mother, understanding the impact and gaining this knowledge was and continues to be truly lifesaving. I believe that for many others, regardless of where you might fall on this spectrum, it is at least life-changing.

What do you think of when you read the word *pollution*? Perhaps you think of black smog bellowing out of an industrial factory's smokestacks, the Great Pacific garbage patch, wildlife covered in oil, mountains of trash in a landfill, or Dr. Seuss's story *The Lorax*? Those are things that come to mind for me. It's natural to picture types of pollution that you can actually see with the naked eye such as air, water, land, and other visual pollution. The Merriam-Webster Dictionary defines pollution as "the action of polluting especially by environmental contamination with man-made waste; also: the condition of being polluted." What does all pollution have in common? Quite simply, all pollution is harmful.

It's obvious and quite easy to identify pollution when you can simply look out your car window as you drive through town and see plastic bags, soda cans, and fast-food wrappers littering the shoulder of the road. In this case, perhaps you will pull over and pick up some trash yourself, or call the city to report it. Most likely, others have also taken notice and have done the same thing. The litter along the road in your town has caught others' attention and people will most likely act on it. Volunteers may gather or the city might send workers to clean it up. Awesome!

What about the less obvious pollution that you can't actually see, like noise pollution? Well, at least you can recognize noise pollution by hearing it! You'll know firsthand if you live or work near an airport, train tracks, a highway, or construction! Perhaps sound-dampening walls have been erected, or restrictive operating hours have been enforced in attempt to lessen the pollution for those in the immediate area.

What about the least obvious type of pollution, radiation pollution? Now, I'm not referencing the nuclear accident in Chernobyl, the meltdown at Fukushima, or the nuclear bombings of Hiroshima and Nagasaki. Those are obvious catastrophic examples, after all. What about the sort of radiation pollution you are exposed to on a regular basis such as that from the countless Wi-Fi networks, cell phones, cell towers and antennae, smart meters, cordless devices, microwave ovens, and such? I believe that at this moment in time, even the average child can identify the air, water, land, and visual pollution sources but the average educated adult can't identify the "invisible" pollution sources, like the radiation examples, which we also refer to as *electrosmog*. Why? Well, for starters, this type of pollution is much "newer" as it is largely occurring in tandem with technology's evolution. Most of the sources didn't exist at their current levels 10 or 20 years ago. I believe the effects are also far less obvious, studied, and understood.

Since visual pollutions can be so easily identified, developing a solution and taking action is far easier, just as in the example of litter along your local road or in the extremely unfortunate and catastrophic event of the Deepwater Horizon oil rig explosion in 2010 in the Gulf of Mexico. Approximately five billion barrels of oil devastated the global environment and ecosystems as a result of that accident. Environmental activists immediately launched campaigns depicting the rescuing of various animals that were covered in oil and near death. It was easy for the average person to observe and understand this issue, which led to taking the next step of taking action. Thousands and thousands of people rallied to the cause and donated money, time, and energy into the ongoing cleanup efforts. The same can't be said for radiation pollution. The general population is not aware of and can't identify the numerous radiation pollution sources let alone take action to manage exposure to it. Our goal with this book is to spread awareness of this issue, share experts' insights and recommendations, and provide solutions and resources for our audience to manage their own exposure to this pollution, which we believe is a silent epidemic that is causing suffering around the world.

I lived, studied, and worked in very densely populated and polluted neighborhoods in Chicago for the past six years, in various high-rise buildings, constantly bombarded by hundreds of different Wi-Fi networks, cell phone towers and antennae, hotspots, smart meters, microwave ovens—you get the idea. Though I am not sensitive to electromagnetic radiation, I notice that my cognitive ability is drastically diminished when exposed to these levels of electromagnetic radiation. I moved into the city of Chicago to attend a university, so this distracting mental fog I felt wasn't exactly promoting an ideal learning environment. The simplest way to test this was taking weekend trips to the less densely populated suburbs and removing myself from that environment. I consistently felt re-energized and that my focus had been restored even after a full day away from the higher levels of radiation pollution. When my mother purchased an electrosmog meter and taught me how to effectively use it to measure electromagnetic radiation, I measured my apartment, my workplace, and the bus, which I spent about five hours riding each week for my work commute. The levels were absolutely off the charts in all of these areas, further confirming my suspicions of this prevalent invisible radiation. I took steps to manage my exposure, where possible, and have felt truly significant results. You can, too.

At my previous job, I spent between two and eight hours per day on the phone. I had to simultaneously use a computer while conversing, so it became difficult to continuously hold the phone with one hand. My employer provided a Bluetooth hands-free headset, which I used for several months. I always wore the wireless headset on my right ear. I began experiencing consistent spasms on my head directly behind my right ear, accompanied by frequent headaches. I hadn't experienced this prior to using the headset, so I had concerns that the headset was the cause. I decided to wean myself off the headset and go back to the handheld desk phone. Within weeks, the spasms and headaches completely stopped. It was worth it to me to forego the convenient headset in return for the health benefit. It's worth considering what long-term effects technologies like this might have on people who actively use headsets. Sometimes convenience isn't always the best choice for your health.

Dan:

I've got good news and bad news. Which do you want to hear first? Okay, your phone, laptop, and smart meter are slowly killing you. The good news is that now you can do something about it.

Less than two years ago, I was in the exact same shoes as you. In case you're looking down at your shoes and you are confused because you see a women's size 6, know that I'm talking about the first time I learned about the dangers of EMFs. If we have anything in common, you were probably thinking the same thing as me: "Holy s***! My cell phone and laptop have been trying to kill me? That's impossible! I thought they were my best friends. " So having been in your current situation, I understand that you're feeling overwhelmed with information and slightly uneasy about the fact that there's an invisible force slowly killing people. Honestly, you should be. By picking up this book, you've already taken an important step in protecting yourself and your loved ones from a silent epidemic. So let's take a deep breath and just take it page-by-page.

Before I tell you my story and why I wrote this book, let's share a few paragraphs to get to know each other. I'll go first. Telling you who I am *not* should be an easier way to begin. I'm not a scientist, medical professional, or an expert on RF. And despite my name being on this cover, I don't really consider myself much of an author either. I'm a 22-year-old that just graduated college, and throughout my life I've spent an unquantifiable amount of time on my cell phone and laptop.

Over the past four years, I lived, worked, studied, and slept amidst all the hustle, bustle, and RF pollution that downtown Chicago has to offer. During college, my laptop became an invaluable full-time extension of my body. If anyone were to ask me how many hours I've spent on my Mac researching topics, writing essays, preparing presentations, or watching Netflix, I would ask them, how many grains of sand are on a beach?

If I wasn't on my laptop, I was on the phone. As former president of my fraternity, I had to be available 24/7 to field calls from any of the 70 members, or dozens of organizations we worked with. Most nights, I slept with my phone in my pillowcase to ensure I'd wake up for a 4 a.m. call. In addition to this, I went to all of my classes in multistory buildings where thousands of other students were on their cell phones and laptops. I worked on the 52nd floor of a high-rise building downtown where I was either on the phone or staring at dual monitors for nine hours at a time. After that, I would put in my Bluetooth headphones and hit the gym. Finally, I'd count sheep for a few hours, less than five feet away from a modem. My entire life I've been getting zapped, yet most days I sleep like a baby, wake up with energy, and avoid white lab coats.

Time to get to know you! Let's start with a few questions. *How many hours per day do you spend on your laptop or cell phone? Does your job require you to be on your laptop or cell phone? When was the last time you left your house without your phone? Do you sleep with a cell phone, laptop, or modem near your bed?*

The point I'm trying to get across is that I get a lot of RF exposure. Depending on how you answered those questions, you probably do too. Want to know the craziest part of it all? It doesn't matter if you're a man or woman, healthy or sick, young or old, happy or sad. You are getting zapped.

Now that we know one another, I want to make three simple points. First, once technology is released and accepted, you can't take it back. Let me explain with a story. I grew up in a quiet suburb of Chicago, right next to a plot of baseball diamonds. If you want to get a taste of my childhood, go watch *The Sandlot*. Throughout my childhood, my friends and I spent sunup to sundown playing pickup baseball games. Looking back, I had a great childhood. One defining moment was in middle school, when my friends and I started getting cell phones. I still recall the dreaded cell phone conversation with my parents, desperately pleading how all of my friends already have them, and how it might save my life in the case of an emergency. They finally gave in, and I got my first cell phone—a pay-as-you-go Boost Mobile flip phone. Although I remember feeling like a kid on Christmas when it turned on for the first time, not much changed after that. Instead of knocking on my friends' doors, I would just call them when I was close.

Fast-forward a couple years, and everything has changed. You can instantly connect with billions of people across the world through social media applications like Facebook. You can get a degree, run your business, buy a pair of shoes, and have dinner delivered to your door without leaving bed. You can know the weather for the whole week without looking out a window and can drive to Vancouver without unfolding a map. The benefits are quite spectacular. But as a society, have we neglected the consequences by placing too much value in the benefits? I believe so. So what do I mean when I say that technology can't be taken back after it's released and accepted? The answer is in the form of a question: When your grandparents have better cell phones than you, would you ever go back to a Motorola RAZR? Don't look to the baby chewing on a tablet for an answer either.

The second point I want to make is that once you become conscious of something, you become responsible for it—especially your health. Although genetics play a role in life, you can control most aspects of your health. You can choose whether you eat organic vegetables or a Wendy's 4 for $4 meal. You can choose whether you spend a day outside or watching three seasons of *Breaking Bad*. You can choose whether you get eight hours of sleep or you go out with friends until 3 a.m. And almost always, your body will start giving you clear signs of whether or not you're making the right choices. When you have a poor diet, your stomach might be upset. When you don't get enough sleep, you feel weak and groggy. When you don't exercise enough, you can see it in the mirror. With EMFs, however, you don't necessarily know when you are getting zapped unless you are EMF hypersensitive, like my mom. So now that you are conscious of RFs, it is your responsibility to at the very least be curious. When technology has become such an integral part of our daily lives, how can we not ask questions about the effects it has on our health? Like I said, I'm not a doctor or expert on RFs. I don't expect you to read this book, take a hammer to your phone, and move to Tibet. I expect you to begin asking more questions about the impact that these devices have on your health. What you discover will determine how you manage your exposure on a daily basis.

My third and final point is that it won't be convenient managing your RF exposure, but neither is having cancer or watching your loved ones have seizures. When I was away at college, I would come home every month or so to see a normally bubbly and energetic woman, bedridden. My mom would be in bed all day, yet she would never sleep or feel rested. She lost her appetite, energy, and ability to leave the house. Even when we would just talk, she would space out and forget what we were talking about. My brothers and I have watched my mom have seizures and have felt completely helpless. All in all, for over two years I had to watch my mom suffer without knowing what was wrong with her or being able to help her. If there is one thing that most living creatures share in common, it is that we would do anything to protect the ones that we love. Doesn't putting your phone in airplane mode seem like such a small price compared to that?

Sure, it's inconvenient having my phone off all day. Friends get irritated, so I recommend having a fun voicemail for them. And yes, it's inconvenient having my laptop connected to an Ethernet cable when sending an email. Your friends get used to calling the landline. All of the inconveniences seem to fade away. In fact, managing my RF exposure has actually improved many aspects of my life that I didn't initially notice. I have much better conversations with my family and friends in person. Have you ever gone to a party where literally every single person is on their cell phone? Well, I have guaranteed that I'll never be at that party, and I just feel much more present conversing when my phone is in airplane mode. Also, my subconscious mind would be bombarded with dozens of various dings, buzzes, rings, and vibrations throughout the typical night. It is amazing how much deeper and faster I sleep when my phone is off. If you don't believe me, try it out yourself. Lastly, I'm able to focus much more in class and in the gym when I don't have to worry about responding to that next text or email. I recommend having multiple blocks in your schedule where you respond to all texts, calls, and emails, rather than keeping your phone on and your health at risk 24/7.

Thankfully, I don't experience any medical problems, and I'd like to keep it that way. I have seen my mom and others reacting to RFs. I know the problem is real. Oddly, when I have my phone silenced and the vibrate feature turned off, I can still feel a vibration prior to a text or call coming in. I can't explain it but it is a real physical sensation that I experience. This is enough proof for me that RFs can affect our bodies. I am hopeful that technology will get safer before it causes any more harm.

Tom:

Five years ago, I began to feel like I was losing my spark. I was always happy but seldom felt energized, and I dismissed it as simply getting older. I was 22 at the time, and the voices of relatives, bosses, teachers, coaches, and parents when I was a kid began rambling in my head: "Someday you'll be old like me, and won't have all that energy, Tom." Was this what they were talking about? Fresh out of college, and I needed to take a nap every day after work to muster up the strength to work out before going right back to bed. Maybe something is wrong with me? Maybe I should see the doctor? I would think about the years before when I ran 60 miles a week. I kept a log of all my runs from freshman year to the summer after my senior year of high school, and I had kept track of nearly 12,000 miles! That was double the mileage that I drove in the first two years I had a drivers license. I could stay up late and get up early and never snoozed my alarm, not once. I loved mornings and mornings loved me. I loved college just as much—the 24 credit quarters, the commute on the 5:12 a.m. train to Union Station, my half-mile walk to the Halsted 8 bus to make my first class, spending the night in the computer lab, working out, and enjoying quality time with friends from all over the world. This sums up my daily routine during my four years of college.

I received a job offer to move to Florida as a supervisor in a hotel six months before graduating. I accepted and moved away, finishing my last two quarters of classes online. Home became a nice apartment with a community pool on a canal that was walking distance to the white-sand beaches of Marco Island, Florida. My new neighbors asked me if I could do them a favor and take their boat out as often as I could to keep it running since they were getting older and didn't get to use it as much. They didn't want to see it sit and deteriorate so needless to say, I took them up on their request of keeping their boat afloat and I got into offshore fishing. I had a good workout routine at the local gym with my friend who was a personal trainer. I stayed in touch with my family and friends back home in Chicago, and I was adjusting well to the new "Salt Life."

My routines remained the same, but waking up slowly became a drag. My workouts were becoming more tiresome, so I decided I'd cut back. I found it difficult to fall asleep, even though I was exhausted. Up until that point in my life, I never drank coffee, but I figured now would be a good time to start. Coffee got me going for about an hour but wasn't the cure. Maybe there was no cure because nothing was wrong. I was just getting old and needed to take naps, that's all. More coffee, more sleep, and more rest days became the solution to my invisible problem.

Life was good and was going to get better after my best friend from college asked me to come work with him in Downtown Chicago. I moved into the city for the first time and got an apartment with both my brothers, something we always talked about doing. My career was going well, but no matter what I did I was exhausted. I would return from work each day and lay down. My pulse would be too high to fall asleep. I would eventually doze off late nights or early mornings but never felt like I got solid rest. Mornings and I fell out of love. I figured it was from the taxi horns, the "L" trains I could hear nearby, and the fast-paced life of living downtown. I thought it would take some getting used to after I settled into the new job.

My job was exciting, and I genuinely enjoyed it. I was a manager at a trendy boutique hotel, and every week I met famous actors and actresses, artists, athletes, comedians—even President Obama stayed on property. Although I didn't get to meet him, I saw him speak, and I spent a weekend showing Secret Service around the hotel for a press conference he held on-site. I helped the FBI catch a robber and got to go on tour with several rock bands. It was an exciting time in my early 20s.

As much fun as it was, like any other job, I spent a lot of time on the phone, emailing, scheduling, doing reports, and crunching numbers from my office. During the busy season, I worked long hours and would spend the night in a hotel room instead of going back to my apartment. I lived less than a mile from the hotel and brought my work home with me. My walkie-talkie could connect from my apartment, so I delegated and made call-ins from home when I wasn't scheduled to work. Even though it wasn't my responsibility, I felt that it was better to get ahead of issues and tasks instead of dealing with them the next day by surprise. I had pride to work hard and found most often that it paid off. My restlessness was attributed to the enthusiasm and energy I was spending on the job.

Fatigue caught up with me after two years, and I began experiencing some strange symptoms which, unknown to me at the time, had a clear culprit. My girlfriend and brothers said that I was too "connected."

Too connected to my phone and email and shouldn't keep my work attached to my hip. They were right, but I eagerly wanted a promotion and wanted to prove to the general manager that I had what it took. It worked! I was promoted.

I had a routine doctor visit and asked him to check out a cluster of strange warts I noticed that had recently developed on my left thigh. He glanced at them and asked me if I carried my phone in that pocket. I told him that I always had my phone on me even when I slept. He stated that they were most likely just ingrown hairs from the friction of my cell phone or keys in my pocket. I was happy to rule out that it wasn't skin cancer from tanning in my short shorts on the beach when I was in Florida with my fair Swedish skin.

My next symptom was one that had been bugging me for nearly a year but didn't seem serious enough to have a doctor check out. I had some aches and pain in my left testicle. I thought that I may have had a mild hernia or strain from working out, which I was continuously doing about three times a week. I figured I wasn't used to the weight I had been lifting and may have gone too heavy one day. I had an ultrasound and was told my pain was due to a testicular varicocele. A varicocele may develop as a result of poorly functioning valves, which are normally found in veins, and can cause infertility. Not an uncommon thing for a male my age to develop. He said that one in six males have this problem and that if it was really causing me discomfort, I could get surgery. He suggested I monitor it and follow up and that I shouldn't worry. This pain persisted until I discovered what RFs are, where they come from, and how they affect our health. I began uncovering hidden truths that have been swept under the rug.

The truth is that I haven't been getting old, I've been getting zapped! Zapped by my cell phone, which I constantly was using, stowed in my left pocket or never further than 6 inches away, even while I slept. Zapped by the phone that I used data to play music apps off of while I worked out in the gym. Zapped by the six smart meters that were congregated just outside my bedroom window at my apartment in Florida. Zapped by my laptop that I spent hundreds of hours on writing papers for school, doing research, and video calling my friends, all from atop the family jewels. Zapped by the Wi-Fi router that I kept on the dresser in my bedroom at both my apartments just an arm's reach from my bedside. Ready for this one? Zapped by the Wi-Fi server tower that casts high-speed Internet throughout the hotel, all the way to the 17th floor and to 300 guest rooms, from MY office! The tower had so many routers that they would overheat if they weren't locked in a room with its own cooling and exhaust system. I used to go in that room when I was cold in the winter. If I wasn't running around in the hotel, I was at my desk, 4 feet from all this radiation. Then I remembered that the same type of tower was just behind the wall from my desk at my previous job.

I began to feel sick just thinking about how many times I've been exposed to dangerous levels of RFs and EMFs just by being an average student, employee, tenant, and citizen. When my mom and I started to uncover our symptoms, it was gut-wrenching at first. I wished I was naïve to all of this newfound knowledge so that I wouldn't have to worry about these problems that I believed were unavoidable. After all, it's the twenty-first century, how can anyone make a living or run a business without a cell phone, Wi-Fi, or data? I can't have access to electricity without a smart meter right?

At the time of writing, I am a full-time event coordinator. I do 80% of my work from a cell phone and email and use modern technology in a sustainable way with low to NO RF exposure! I want to share my experience with overexposure to radio frequencies, which is not one of any major tragedy but one that I think many can relate to whether they realize it or not. I believe RFs and 5G (which has not yet been rolled out as of this writing) are the single most dangerous and corrupt issues of our lifetime. Yet everyone is so addicted to their relationship to technology that they fear admitting it or making any changes. I encourage anyone who wants to know more about how strong these frequencies are to research and borrow or purchase an RF meter and experiment with your cell phone, smart meter, router, and areas of your house, car, and workplace. Read about the effects other people are experiencing. Understand that whether you seem to notice any effects or not, this is affecting you and the people around you. It is going to get worse if you don't do something about it.

What can you do about it? Educate yourself on this topic and read this book cover to cover. Pass it along to a friend when you have completed it. A wise person once said, "To know and not to do, is not to know". If this information resonates with you, make a change because simply knowing what to do will not protect you unless you take action.

I have managed to run a business and maintain my relationships with my girlfriend, friends, and family without living under a rock. I still use my computer and phone daily with a thousand times less exposure and have done so for nearly two years. I no longer have constant fatigue, testicular pain, frequent headaches, restlessness, or loss of appetite. Even the warts on my leg and thumb have since disappeared. I've been able to connect the dots and figure out what was causing my symptoms and to feel like a healthy 26-year-old should!

Susan:

While I tell my story later in the book, my main reason for wanting to co-author this book is to alert people to the risks. Most people have no idea what is lurking in their pockets, homes, workplaces, and playgrounds. As an investigative health coach for nearly two decades, I considered myself to be at the forefront of health-related issues. I had helped thousands of people to think outside the box and come up with solutions to their health challenges. After several years of declining health, it was not until I fell gravely ill that I figured out the cause of my suffering. I had no idea that RFs could make people so sick. Now, I struggle on a daily basis to live in my own home, to go out in public to do the things I enjoy, to be able to work outside my shielded home, and to travel and speak, which is one of my biggest passions. I can no longer do simple things like go to a restaurant with friends and family without considering my exposure and suffering the consequences of being in an environment near cell antennae, smart meters, with other people using their cell phones, Wi-Fi, and cordless phones.

I can no longer go to a concert, play, or movie theatre without being shielded and taking special precautions. For now, I choose to continue living my life doing some of the things I love to do, but I suffer the consequences of that choice. At some point, I may not be able to continue living with those options. Each day, I feel those freedoms slipping away.

I don't know if the infrastructure that is in place will be replaced with a safer technology in my lifetime. I live my life in small increments, seeking refuge whenever possible in remote areas of the country that are currently safe enough for me to recover a bit from the day-to-day exposures I inadvertently get. As 5G, the fifth generation of wireless technology is rolled out, I fear there will be nowhere for me to go. No place to seek refuge. The thought of being confined to a barricaded structure does not seem fair to me. I want to be an active and productive member of society and to lead a meaningful life.

I have met and interviewed about 40 others who suffer as I do. I fear that more and more people and animals will begin to suffer in much the same way. Studies show that 3–15% of the world's population are experiencing symptoms of radiofrequency exposure. Many are sick and do not know that technology may be the cause. When I began searching on the Internet, I was amazed at all of the information that is out there. The trouble is, I never knew there were potential dangers associated with these devices. You don't hear about this unless you are looking for it. If we don't stop using technological devices without taking precautions, more people will suffer from EHS. We are playing roulette with our health and that of our future generations. We have the right to be safe in our own homes and communities. We have the right to know if the devices we buy might be harming our health. We deserve to know if there are health consequences to the frequencies we are being exposed to without our consent. We must demand safer technology. We must ensure that technologies and the frequencies they transmit are adequately studied by independent scientists prior to imposing these technologies and frequencies on the public.

I did not know I was being harmed until it was too late. I feel that the average person is completely unaware of the dangers we are facing. My sons and I are on a mission to change that with our book. I have devoted my life to sharing this information on as big of a scale as I can and have teamed up with others who are dedicated to making a difference. While I do not know how to undo the damage at this time, I will continue to work on exploring anything that feels feasible to me. It is unacceptable to me that I have been damaged by this technology and may not be able to regain my health and brain capacity.

There are brilliant scientists, engineers, and innovators capable of developing and implementing safe technologies. We are not against technology. We want safe technology. We want accountability. We don't want the population to be exposed to any level of radiation that has not been proven safe. If we don't act on this now, there is a good possibility that each of us will personally suffer the consequences with physical issues or with the emotional pain of watching others suffer. I do not want to look back at the end of my life and ask, *"Why didn't I do more?"*

Chapter 3

What You Need to Know About Electromagnetic Radiation

Before we dive into this section, we want you to know that this is the most technical part of the book. If the content feels complicated, we urge you to skim over or read past the complicated parts. It is not necessary to understand the frequencies or the measurements. The most important thing you can take from this book is to understand the potential risks of electromagnetic radiation and to feel empowered to take action steps to reduce your exposure.

This chapter will provide you with a basic understanding of electromagnetic radiation and explain why the guidelines that are in place may not be as protective as we would expect.

What Is Microwave Radiation?

Electromagnetic radiation (EMR) includes magnetic fields, electric fields, dirty electricity, and radiofrequency radiation. This book focuses mainly on wireless radiofrequency radiation in the microwave range.

Any device or appliance which communicates or transmits information wirelessly generates radiofrequency. Examples include cellular phones, digital cordless landline phones, Bluetooth devices, cell phone masts, cellular antenna transmitters, remote-controlled toys, wireless gaming systems, wireless security systems, autonomous vehicles, transmitting smart meters, and two-way radios. While a microwave oven, formerly known as a radar range, generally does not communicate information wirelessly unless it is a smart appliance, it generates microwave radiation while it is running. That is how it cooks your food.

The terms radiofrequency (RF), radiofrequency radiation (RFR), radio waves, microwaves, or microwave radiation are used interchangeably in this work.

For ease of presentation, we will consider any device which plugs into an electrical outlet or is hardwired into your electrical wiring to be capable of producing electromagnetic fields (EMF) or extremely low frequency electromagnetic fields (ELF-EMF). These are generated by our non-wireless electric appliances. Anything that is wired or carries voltage along its wires produces an electrical field. Examples include the wiring in your home, the wiring which carries electricity to homes and businesses, an electrical outlet, a blow dryer, a refrigerator, a toaster, a lamp, a fan, and an alarm clock. ELF-EMFs can cause health effects. High-tension power lines produce low-frequency emissions, yet you probably would not want to live under them.

Any device or appliance which plugs into an outlet or is hardwired and also communicates wirelessly produces both EMFs and RFs. Examples of such devices are a computer, Wi-Fi router, cordless DECT telephone, smart thermostat, baby monitor, or any smart appliance.

The Electromagnetic Spectrum

Radiofrequency is a form of electromagnetic radiation. There are two types of electromagnetic radiation. On one end of the electromagnetic spectrum is ionizing radiation. Ionizing radiation is the form of radiation emitted by X-rays, CT scans, mammograms, gamma rays, and radon. Ionizing radiation is known to cause cancer. Ionizing radiation strips electrons from atoms and molecules. There is agreement among scientists that ionizing radiation breaks bonds, damages DNA, and harms the body.

On the other end of the spectrum is non-ionizing radiation. There are both natural and man-made sources of non-ionizing radiation. Non-ionizing radiation is emitted naturally as visible, infrared, and ultraviolet light produced by the sun. There are natural EMFs that come from the earth and are beneficial to life. Man-made sources of non-ionizing radiation come from electricity, electromagnetic fields, and radio waves. They are emitted by any appliances that have electricity running through them and by devices which communicate wirelessly such as cell phones and Wi-Fi routers.

When you make a call, send a text, or transmit data from your phone or via Wi-Fi, it is done via non-ionizing radiofrequency radiation.

Although all scientists do not agree that non-ionizing radiation in itself causes cancer, many scientists believe that it does. Some argue that it does not produce the energy required to remove electrons from atoms or molecules. Industries tell us non-ionizing radiation does not cause health effects.

Man-made radio waves have various frequencies. The frequency is the number of electromagnetic waves passing a specific point in one second. Frequencies are measured in hertz (Hz), which is one cycle per second. A megahertz (MHz) is one million cycles per second. A gigahertz (GHz) is one billion cycles per second.

Different cellular networks operate in different frequency ranges, for instance, GSM uses 900 to 1,800 MHz, UMTS uses 1,900 to 2,170 MHz, and LTE uses 800 to 2,600 MHz. As an increasing numbers of devices are used to download or transmit data at faster speeds, more bandwidth is needed. In order to accommodate all of this data, the proposed 5G, or fifth generation of wireless technology, will operate from the lower ranges up to the

30 to 300 GHz range, in the high frequency millimeter wave (MMW) band.

Thermal vs. Non-thermal

One type of biological effect from exposure to electromagnetic radiation is a heating of, or temperature rise in, the body and its sensitive organs, which results from absorbing electromagnetic power. Temperature distribution patterns of that heat vary from person to person, depending on body makeup, body constitution, and the exact location of the device and the frequency and pattern of the waves transmitting from it. For protection from thermal effects, the best strategy is distance. You can reduce or eliminate the risk simply by being mindful about how close you are to your phone or devices.

Non-thermal effects are those biological effects that occur at levels that do not heat tissue. For protection from non-thermal effects, distance helps, but you must also stop or block the source.

In 1996, the FCC issued guidelines for RF radiation exposure. These have not been updated since, despite the huge increase in exposure to different frequencies and pulsations that has occurred since then. These guidelines only relate to thermal damage. They tell us that if there is no thermal damage, there is no harm done.

Where is the evidence that non-thermal levels are safe? If you don't look at the studies that show non-thermal microwave radiation causes harm, or if you fail to study something, it does not mean it is safe. Ignorance is not bliss. Ignoring this issue will not cause it to stop harming us. The story is painfully similar to that of tobacco or asbestos. Some day we may be sorry that we didn't heed the warnings. We will regret that we failed to take the emerging evidence seriously.

There are many research papers that conclude that cell phones and radiofrequency radiation do not cause harm. Industry studies support the belief that there is no harm caused by radiofrequency radiation. They maintain that the only possible damage of non-ionizing radiation comes at levels that cause thermal damage, which is through electro-stimulation, or heating of the tissue. Most agree that thermal damage can cause cancer. There is much confusion, and many studies show conflicting results.

I have found references to thousands of independent studies that show the potential harm to the body that are not based on heating of tissue. Our position is that if there is the possibility of harm, you deserve to be warned.

In Chapter 5, we provide an overview of some of the evidence and the research from scientists who support the belief that microwave radiation is causing non-thermal harm. There is a large body of international scientific consensus that there are many non-thermal health effects. Industry does not look at this research. This information comes from respected scientists who have the credentials to speak about this issue.

Are You Breaking the Rules?

Do you hold a phone in your hand or against your face? Do you store it in your pocket or against your body? Do you hold a laptop on your lap? If you do, you may be violating the safety rules.

Did you know that cell phone manufacturers tell us not to allow cell phones to touch our body? When you look around on any crowded sidewalk, store, or look at people driving or riding on public transportation, the majority of the people using their phones are holding them in their hand or up to their head.

Many people talk on their cell phones for more than 10 or 20 minutes at a time. This can cause thermal changes (heating) of their hands, fingers, face, ear, and brain. Look over your cell phone records to get a true picture of how many minutes you talk on your phone.

Most of us have used a laptop on our laps. It is not by chance that manufacturers have changed the name of laptop computers to notebooks. They are aware of the fact that heating your lap and its nearby sensitive parts can be harmful.

What is going to happen to these people who are violating the safety guidelines years down the road? What will happen to them if they are violating these standards every day for ten or twenty years? What if thermal risk was only a small part of the hazards of smart technology? How much risk are you willing to take? What if the safety guidelines are off by a factor of many times, as many researchers warn?

Chapter 4

Cell Phones

In 2017, the California Department of Public Health issued guidelines warning people to limit their use of cell phones. It also recommends using your speakerphone and keeping the phone away from the body (California Department of Public Health 2017). This is due to the link between electromagnetic radiation and brain cancer. In 2011, the International Agency for Research on Cancer (IARC) of the World Health Organization (WHO) classified radiofrequency electromagnetic fields from mobile phones as Group 2B carcinogens, which means these fields are possibly carcinogenic, or cancer-causing, to humans. Many scientists agree they should be classified as a carcinogen.

We assume the standards are protecting us, but they are not. They are simply guidelines that are based on the ability of the device to cause heating of the tissue, which occurs when the device is touching your body or in very close proximity to it.

According to the June 2, 2018 edition of the Sun, mobile phone companies, such as Blackberry and Nokia, are warning shareholders about the potential health risks of radio signals but aren't telling their customers. The report states it "can't provide absolute assurance" that there isn't a link between radiofrequency emissions and health risks (Hawkin 2018). Companies have a duty to warn their shareholders when there is a threat of damage or liability that would lead to a profit loss or decrease the value of the company. You don't find these companies sending messages to their consumers to warn them of the possible danger and telling them how to use their phones in a safer manner.

It is concerning that the cell phone industry denies most claims of damage. Cell phone manufacturers warn that you should hold your phone no less than about an inch away from the body; however, most people do not read the fine print. The warnings are often buried in the manual or in your phone's settings. If the industry issued warnings on phones, many people would use their phones the same way, just as is the case with warnings on tobacco products. There are billions of cell phone users in the world. The truth is most people do not know there is a danger related to cell phones and wireless devices and would take some precautions if they knew this. Cell phone sales would probably remain the same even with the warnings, but at least people would know to protect themselves and use their phones more responsibly. Many people, especially teenagers, are on their phones constantly and even sleep with their phones on their bed, next to their bed, or under their pillow. This increases the risk of serious health consequences.

According to Dr. Dariusz Leszczynski, molecular biologist, research professor, and advisor to the World Health Organization (WHO) on radiation safety, most people with smart phones are breaching the safely limits of their devices, and the current safety limits do not protect all users (Leszczynski 2017).

Specific Absorption Rate

The Specific Absorption Rate (SAR) value is a measurement of the amount or radiofrequency that is absorbed by the body tissues. While a cell phone is rated with a SAR value, there is no consideration or regulation on exposure from multiple sources simultaneously. In addition, the SAR value only takes into consideration the heating of body tissue from the device. It does not address the potential non-thermal impact.

"The FCC's exposure guidelines specify limits for human exposure to RF emissions from handheld mobile phones in terms of Specific Absorption Rate (SAR), a measure of the rate of absorption of RF energy by the body. The safe limit for a mobile phone user is a SAR of 1.6 watts per kg (1.6 W/kg), averaged over one gram of tissue" (Federal Communications Commission 2015).

Cell phones are not meant to be touching our bodies. Holding them to your head while talking or carrying them in your pocket or your bra can cause harm by heating your tissue and subjecting you to high levels of RF radiation. Remember, the current guidelines are based on the thermal effects from the devices.

It is important to note that when you are in an area of weak reception, your phone must work harder. A California Department of Public Health research study showed that radiofrequency exposure is up to 10,000 times more intense in an area of weak reception than in an area with strong signal strength (Wall et al. 2018).

Chapter 5

Evidence of Harm

The International EMF Scientist Appeal presented to the United Nations, first written in 2015, now has over 240 signatures from 41 nations representing the world's top scientists who study radiofrequency and non-ionizing radiation. They are in agreement that:

Numerous recent scientific publications have shown that EMF affects living organisms at levels well below most international and national guidelines. Effects include increased cancer risk, cellular stress, increase in harmful free radicals, genetic damages, structural and functional changes of the reproductive system, learning and memory deficits, neurological disorders, and negative impacts on general well-being in humans. Damage goes well beyond the human race, as there is growing evidence of harmful effects to both plant and animal life.

These findings justify our appeal to the United Nations (UN) and, all member States in the world, to encourage the World Health Organization (WHO) to exert strong leadership in fostering the development of more protective EMF guidelines, encouraging precautionary measures, and educating the public about health risks, particularly risk to children and fetal development. By not taking action, the WHO is failing to fulfill its role as the preeminent international public health agency. (EMFscientist.org 2015; printed with permission)

The biggest tragedy is that no one is hearing this message. Did you get the memo? We certainly didn't. Hundreds of the world's leading scientists studying non-ionizing radiation are trying to warn us about the dangers of non-ionizing radiation. They have either done the research or reviewed the studies. They are appealing to the United Nations to try to protect you.

Experts Warn of the Dangers

As we saw in the appeal statement, there are many body systems affected and many disorders caused by non-ionizing radiation. Scientists have known about this and have been studying the dangers of radio waves at non-thermal levels for decades.

In 1972, US Naval Medical Research Institute published a revised bibliography of over 2200 references documenting the biological effects of radiofrequency radiation (Glaser 1972). The majority of these studies relate to the effects of non-ionizing radiation on humans. They note about 130 different symptoms and disorders caused by microwave radiation. The studies found changes in physiology, the central nervous system, the autonomic nervous system, the peripheral nervous system, the vascular system, and the endocrine glands. They found this radiation caused psychological disorders, behavioral disorders, blood disorders, biochemical disorders, metabolic disorders, genetic and chromosomal damage, and mutations.

The BioInitiative Report first published in 2007 and updated in 2012 is a comprehensive list of several thousand published studies compiled by world experts in science, medicine, and public policy (BioInitiative Working Group 2012). It looks at the biological effects of exposure and is a clear and compelling case for our exposure guidelines being much too lenient.

Many scientists agree that EMR poses the single biggest threat to human health of the twenty-first century. You can't see or feel how it is affecting you. It is an invisible threat that may be causing havoc in your body. It is affecting you physically and energetically. There have been thousands of studies raising concern about cell phones, Wi-Fi, and smart meters. Yet, industry denies any claims and reassures us that these devices are safe. Despite all the controversy, there is enough evidence of harm that we can't dismiss this.

Throughout this book, we will share our own experiences with electromagnetic radiation, what we have figured out through taking numerous measurements, and what we learned from interviewing others who experience health effects from radiation.

Because we are not experts in electromagnetic radiation, microwave technology, physics, or physiology, we wanted you to hear from those who are. We found comments from some of the people we consider to be experts in the fields of microwave radiation, from those who research public health issues, and from leaders in conducting scientific research on the potential risks of electromagnetic radiation exposure. We thought you might want to know what some of these experts are saying.

The late Robert O. Becker, MD once said, "The greatest polluting element in the earth's environment is the proliferation of electromagnetic fields" (quoted in Goodreads 2018). He was a man ahead of his time and was devoted to understanding the truth at all costs. He warned, "All life pulsates in time to the Earth and our artificial fields cause abnormal reactions in all organisms. … Increasing electropollution could set in motion irreversible changes leading to our extinction" (quoted in Goodreads 2018).

Frank Clegg, Canadians for Safe Technology and former head of Microsoft Canada, states that no one can say that microwave radiofrequencies are safe. Safety standards only look at thermal effects. If tissue is not heated, it is considered not to cause harm (quoted in Demasi 2016).

Dr. Devra Davis, PhD, MPH, epidemiologist and internationally renowned scientist who also was the founding director of the Board on Environmental Studies and Toxicology of the US National Research Council and president of Environmental Health Trust, says there is a growing body of evidence showing that prenatal exposure to cell phone radiation causes serious defects in the offspring. She states that you have the right to know that your mobile phone should not be kept near your testicles, ovaries, breasts, heart, or brain (Davis 2017).

Joel M. Moskowitz, Ph.D., Director, Center for Family and Community Health, School of Public Health, University of California, Berkeley, summarizes peer-reviewed research on health risks associated with wireless radiation. He recently posted a summary of the National Toxicology Program (NTP) final reports on the effects of two years of exposure to 2G (GSM and CDMA) cell phone radiation on rats and mice at non-thermal levels, 19 years after the NTP was asked to conduct the study. The study found "clear evidence" of increased cancer risk in male rats, particularly heart schwanommas, a type of tumor, found "some evidence" of brain cancer, and measurable DNA damage (Moskowitz 2018).

Interestingly, the effects of cell phone radiation on overall tumor risk did not demonstrate a simple dose-response relationship. The highest overall risk was found with three watts per kilogram of exposure, not six watts per kilogram. Male rats exposed to three watts per kilogram of cell phone radiation were the most likely to develop cancer somewhere in their body. Forty-two to forty-five percent of rats exposed to this level of cell phone radiation developed cancer, as compared to only twenty-seven percent of control rats. Moreover, 73–76% of male rats in the lowest exposure groups, 1.5 watts per kilogram, had higher rates of benign tumors as compared to 54% of rats in the control group (Moskowitz 2018).

The Ramazzini Institute in Italy performed a life-span study on rats to determine if RFR caused cancer. They found an increase in the incidence of tumors of the brain and heart in exposed rats (Falcioni et al. 2018).

Dr. Magda Havas, PhD, toxicologist and researcher, teaches courses about electromagnetic pollution at Trent University and says, "We are electromagnetic … we respond to external sources of electromagnetic frequencies in a variety of ways that can be either beneficial or harmful" (2018). In her research, she has found that radiation from a cordless phone causes heart arrhythmia, tachycardia (rapid heart rate), and alters the sympathetic and parasympathetic nervous system similar to a fight-or-flight stress response. She states, "We all need to make informed decisions on how to use modern electromagnetic technology effectively and safely" (Havas 2018).

According to Dr. Martin Pall, Professor Emeritus of Biochemistry and Basic Medical Sciences at Washington State University, EMFs act by activating the voltage-gated calcium channels that are in the plasma membranes around our cells. Most biological effects are produced by excess calcium in the cells (Pall 2013). Non-thermal microwave exposure attacks our endocrine system and our nervous system, which leads to widespread neurological effects. He believes the current safety standards allow us to be exposed to levels of microwave radiation that are about 7 million times too high (Pall 2018).

In the press release for the 2012 BioInitiative Report, Dr. David Carpenter, MD, Director, Institute for Health and the Environment, University at Albany and coeditor of the BioInitiative Report, states: "There is now much more evidence of risks to health affecting billions of people worldwide. The status quo is not acceptable in light of the evidence for harm" (Carpenter 2013).

Dr. Dietrich Klinghardt, MD, PhD, a practicing physician in the United States and Germany specializing in chronic illness, states that man-made electromagnetic frequencies in the high frequency range are devastating to our health. These frequencies alter our brain proteins which affect virtually all cellular functions. In his medical practices, he sees a number of symptoms and illnesses related to radiofrequency exposure. These include insomnia; depression; neurological symptoms such as tingling, numbness, and vibrations in the body; muscle aches; fatigue; headaches; learning disabilities; and autism. He has seen devastating consequences from smart meters and says they pose one of the most significant threats to our health. According to Dr. Klinghardt, this electromagnetic pollution is an emerging health risk and even those who are not sensitive or experiencing symptoms are being harmed (Klinghardt 2012).

In addition to all of this, RFR has been shown to increase blood-brain barrier permeability (Sirav and Seyhan 2011). This is alarming because the blood-brain barrier prevents toxins, bacteria, and heavy metals from entering our brains.

How Do We Interpret This and What Can We Take Away?

It is sometimes hard to interpret the studies. We tried to give an overview with a brief summary and provide links if anyone would like to take a deeper dive into learning more about the studies. This is really the tip of the iceberg. There are thousands of studies showing potential harm. We did not intend to overwhelm you with science but wanted you to see that this is not hearsay or being made up. The bottom line is that our devices are causing harm and we are not being told about the risk. Wireless radiation at non-thermal levels causes many health effects.

The way I like to think of it is that when RF radiation comes in contact with our body, it first impacts our skin. These man-made frequencies irritate the skin and cause the cells to secrete stress hormones and other factors that circulate through our body. Our body goes into a fight-or-flight state. When the voltage in our bodies is high enough, it affects our cell membranes so they cannot properly carry out their normal functions. The chemical processes that normally occur at a cellular level are suppressed. Our cellular metabolism becomes disrupted. An imbalance occurs in the calcium levels in and around our cells. Some things that may occur as a result are our normal hormonal cycles can be disrupted, and it may cause sleep disturbances. We may have increases in free radical damage and oxidative stress. In addition, we may experience mitochondrial dysfunction, our energy levels may be affected, inflammatory processes may be initiated, brain proteins may be altered, DNA may be damaged. We may have trouble detoxifying, causing a toxic build up in our body as cells cannot purge their waste products, and we may become unable to properly assimilate nutrients, which can manifest any number of different symptoms and diseases over time. The bottom line is that our bodies are unable to function at an optimal level, and many functions become impaired.

Traditional medical belief is that sunburn resulting from an hour or two of intense sun exposure at age 3 can cause skin cancer 20, 30, or even 50 years later. The symptoms of sunburn, which is essentially an overexposure to solar radiation, are chills, nausea, burning skin, and exhaustion. They are similar to the complaints of those who have been overexposed to wireless radiation. People who have had skin cancer or died from it may have wished they would have known the risk 30 years ago while they were working on their tropical tan. They may have done things differently back then that could have spared them the prognosis. They may have limited their time in the sun, worn protective fabrics, or sunscreen. The good news for those of us reading this book is that we now have a warning about wireless radiation and we can take actions to protect ourselves and perhaps prevent some of the damage that may otherwise show up at some point down the road.

It is important to realize how difficult it is to study the impact of all of the radiation we are exposed to and to monitor its affect on the entire population. As a former research scientist who has worked on studies that have been published in peer-reviewed scientific journals, and as a former editor for scientific papers submitted for publication to scientific journals, I can tell you this is not easy to study on people living in a metropolitan area where they may have the highest exposures. The study must be done over the long term, over many years and even over decades. Technology changes so frequently that it is hard to design a truly meaningful study. The 5G technology will roll out in select cities in 2019, and we have no idea what the impact will be. We do know that radiation exposure seems to be cumulative, so it makes sense that over time, more and more people will suffer the consequences.

It is also impossible to shield the control group that is living amongst the general population. If they can find people for control groups who do not use cell phones, they have to consider that those people are constantly being bombarded with radiofrequencies from numerous other sources, such as Wi-Fi, microwave ovens, smart meters, and other people's cell phones. If a person is a control subject in a cell phone study and does not use a cell phone but stands in front of their microwave oven as they heat their lunch, sleeps ten feet away from a smart meter, has a cordless phone in their home, or rides in a car, bus, or train where other people are using cell phones, they may develop some of the same symptoms as those subjects using smart phones. It is simply impossible to create a controlled exposure for this type of study. That negates the impact of those symptoms in the cell phone users in the study. It is impossible to have a true control group to compare in this setting. Therefore it will be hard to get meaningful data.

It is hard to extrapolate from a short-term study on mice in a controlled environment and know what that information really means to us living in the real world. Most studies do not look at long-term low-level exposures like the ones we are chronically exposed to. We need more truly independent research that is done over long periods of time and mimics real-life exposures from multiple sources. This will take many years. In the meantime, take precautions to protect yourself. Consider this information and use common sense. We all need to be smart about the issue of radiation exposure and exercise caution whenever possible.

Why Should You Care?

If you are questioning whether you are being overexposed, the answer is yes. If you carry a cell phone, are frequently in a Wi-Fi area, have a cordless phone, or spend time in close proximity to a cell tower, you may be subjected to harmful levels of radiation. We are all being overexposed.

According to Nielson, a market research group, the average US adult spends 3 hours and 48 minutes a day on their devices. The truth is that we don't know what the cumulative impact is from all of our exposure. You probably shouldn't listen to anyone who tells you they know how you are being affected or not being affected by the exposure you are getting. Each of our bodies responds differently to our electromagnetic environment.

We acknowledge that there are conflicting beliefs on this issue and that many studies show no health effects. Industry assures us that science says this is safe, that anyone who says otherwise is a quack, and there is no need for you to be concerned about any health threats. Just trust us, and keep buying our products.

When things are discovered in science, they are often ridiculed at first and then discredited and debated before they are accepted as truth. We believe the truth is the one thing that will protect us in the end.

Environmental Concerns

There is also evidence to suggest the fact that birds, bees, agricultural animals, trees, and vegetation are adversely affected by RFs. The rapidly declining bee population and colony collapse are getting worldwide attention because bees are responsible for pollinating the majority of the crops that become our food. One study found cell phone radiation can influence honey bees' behavior and physiology (Kumar et al. 2011). It was also noted that the bees became slightly aggressive and started beating their wings in agitation. Another found a decline in colony strength, in the egg laying rate of the queen, and in the honey and pollen in the colony after exposure to EMR (Sharma and Kumar 2010).

In a research paper which reviewed 113 published studies, scientists found that two-thirds of the studies reported that RF affected the health of birds, insects, animals, and plants (Cucurachi et al. 2013).

RFs raise concern for migratory birds and insects because they may alter the receptor organs and impair their ability to orient in the magnetic field of the earth (Balmori 2015). This can disrupt their navigational systems.

We have seen many well-established bushes and plants die after a smart meter was installed in close proximity. All of our indoor plants and herbs that were within 10 feet of our smart meters have died, with the exception of the succulents.

We Don't Have a Choice

For many years, I worked in laboratory settings with toxic chemicals. I worked to replace chemicals that caused cancer, birth defects, or other negative health effects. I always used these chemicals to compare the effectiveness of new replacement chemicals. I knew the risk of using these chemicals. For several companies, I managed the employee Right to Know information and the hazardous waste disposal, and I was often exposed to these toxic materials. I took every precaution possible but was often inadvertently exposed. Many times a rubber glove would tear or break down while I was wearing it, a chemical would splash or spill onto an unprotected area of my body, a respirator would fail and I would breathe fumes, and at times I would break a thermometer and do a mercury cleanup without always having the proper protective equipment. I accepted the responsibility. I felt it was my duty as a scientist to get the job done and sort of "take one for the team." Eventually I realized that these exposures were harming my health and began to question the cumulative, long-term risks. I was no longer willing to accept these exposures and made the choice to get out of working in the lab under these conditions to protect my health.

Unlike most other toxic exposures in life, we don't have a choice with EMR. We can chose whether or not we want to eat junk food, GMOs, or fast food. We can choose if we want to consume alcohol. We choose if and when we want to drink diet soda. We choose whether we drink tap water or filtered water. We can choose if we want to work in an industry that uses a lot of toxic chemicals. We can choose if we want to smoke or allow someone to smoke in our home. We can choose to go to establishments where smoking is permitted, or we can choose to avoid those places. With EMR we don't have a choice. We can't control our RF exposure in public or the amount of radiation that penetrates our homes.

Do You Feel Lucky?

There have been many studies indicating that RFs pose a serious threat to our health. You have to decide how much risk you are willing to take. At this time, we know our exposure is cumulative and there can be a long latency period for diseases to develop. Many people worldwide are reacting to overexposure. We do not know if electromagnetic sensitivity is reversible and if there is a cure or simple solution to the problem.

So far, we have shared a lot of information about technology and how it harms us. No one knows their own threshold for tolerating radiofrequency radiation until they reach it. It can happen in an instant. While no one can say for certain that this is going to get a lot worse before it gets better, all the evidence points in that direction. It is imperative that we are proactive and take precautions for ourselves and future generations. In the next sections, we share personal stories of those affected and key strategies to reduce radiation and protect our living environment.

SECTION II

Electrohypersensitivity: When Technology Torments Our Lives

Electrohypersensitivity (EHS), electro-sensitivity (ES), microwave sickness, and radio wave sickness are terms which describe a condition where the body has strong adverse physical reactions to the electromagnetic radiation of common technological devices. The condition is marked by the awareness that radiation is causing the problem.

The fact that RFs at non-thermal levels cause harm cannot be denied. Most of the advanced nations of the world have been studying radio waves as military weapons for over 50 years. RFs can be directed at an individual or a crowd to break up riots, protestors, or to disable a perpetrator. They have also been used intentionally to make people sick. During the Cold War, in a case referred to as the Moscow Signal, Soviets were directing microwaves at frequencies similar to Wi-Fi routers and cell phones at employees of the United States Embassy in Moscow for roughly 20 years. Many of the embassy employees complained of varying health effects, ranging from ringing in the ears and headaches to infertility and cancers (Elwood 2012). More recently it has been determined that the health effects experienced by US and Canadian diplomats at the United States Embassy in Cuba are consistent with those exposed to pulsed radiofrequency radiation (Golomb 2018). While the investigation is ongoing, it should be alarming to us that some of the same frequencies used as military weapons to attack people are being generated by common devices in our homes. The health effects of these weapons have been studied and well-documented for decades.

When something that is harmful takes a long time to result in disease, it is difficult to prove the exact cause. The argument could be made that if someone is a smoker and gets lung cancer, that the cigarettes were probably the cause. But in some cases, people smoke for 50 or 60 years and don't get cancer. In other cases, some people who have never smoked get lung cancer. This can cause confusion, and industries benefit when confusion among concerned customers is generated.

Everyone's body is different and will react differently to different exposures. While a portion of the population is becoming aware of how technology is harming them, most people have no idea that this is the case.

EHS comes with many different symptoms. Some react only to sources of radiofrequency such as Wi-Fi or their cell phone, while others react to other electromagnetic fields or dirty electricity that comes from electrical appliances and wiring.

While traditional medicine does not recognize EHS as a disease, it is a devastating condition and it is becoming more widespread. Sweden considers EHS a functional impairment and has several hundred thousand residents considered to be electro-sensitive. While some claim EHS is psychosomatic, we can assure you it is not. It is a real problem with real physical consequences. There are probably several million people worldwide experiencing EHS.

While most people do not notice any reaction to EMR, at a cellular level, everyone is being affected. Some people notice subtle reactions while others experience extreme physical and mental suffering as a result of their exposures. It is a natural response of the body to get sick from these man-made frequencies. The body's functions are electrically orchestrated and these frequencies upset that natural, innate balance. While some may be more resilient than others, everyone must understand the impact this is having on our bodies.

Susan has suffered tremendously from EHS before ever having heard of it. This chapter will give you a very detailed personal and medical account of her experience. At times, it may seem like too much information, but it was done intentionally so you could follow her train of thought, understand her passion for the problem, and perhaps relate to some of the symptoms and feelings she experienced.

Since first publishing a chapter about the problems associated with radiofrequency radiation in 2018 in her book *Bridging Medicine and Miracles*, Susan has been contacted by dozens of people who report they have been suffering from the same issues. She also has a number of clients who suffer from this reaction. We have interviewed many people who are affected by EMR to varying degrees. In a subsequent chapter, we will share some of their stories.

Chapter 6

Susan Tells Her Story

In 2015, I received a notice on my front door that my power company had installed a smart meter on my house. If you are not familiar, a smart meter is a utility meter which sends your usage data to the provider wirelessly without the need for someone to come out and take a reading at your home. They can be used to monitor your consumption of electricity, gas, and water.

I was not happy with the idea of this "gift" of a smart meter because I knew it gave my power company personal data about me that they could sell to marketing companies. I felt it was more an issue of data mining and an invasion of privacy than a threat to my personal health. I had some concerns though. At the time, I had a meter that measures extremely low frequency (ELF) EMFs. I placed my EMF meter close to the smart meter to see what type of measurements I might find. The readings were extremely high near the smart meter, which is also next to the main power supply coming into the house. Away from the smart meter, the readings were low. I also measured inside of the house, since the adjacent room is Will's bedroom when he is in town. Everything appeared fine as long as it was not within about five feet of the meter.

Soon after the smart meter was installed, I began to notice that I was having trouble sleeping. I run on less sleep than most people because I am usually feverishly working on a book or some research that has me pretty well consumed. This was different. I was tired but could not sleep. If I did fall asleep, I would awaken an hour later and was wide awake. I dismissed any correlation between this problem and the smart meter because the readings were low and I was on the opposite side of the house. I went on a couple of wild-goose chases for answers, but never could fully figure it out. I started experiencing shortness of breath, spikes in blood pressure, and very high resting pulse rates. All of this would happen when I was not doing anything physical. I had an electrocardiogram (ECG) and an echocardiogram to rule out any heart condition. Other than the extremely fast pulse, neither test showed evidence of any heart problem. I developed constant twitching throughout my body in numerous locations at once. The sensation would travel around my body in random patterns. I had an electromyogram (EMG) to rule out a neurological issue such as Parkinson's or ALS. The results were within the normal range.

I saw several doctors over the next several months. At this point in time, I was only getting two to three hours of sleep per day. I was exhausted from sleep deprivation and began to have problems focusing and functioning. One doctor attributed this to anxiety. That didn't make sense. I am more at peace than most people I know, and I know how to release my stress. I did not believe it was an anxiety issue. My labs were all out of range—my liver enzymes were elevated, and my iron and thyroid levels were fluctuating—but nothing jumped out as the specific cause of these issues. Another doctor suggested hyperthyroidism, which matched my symptoms. Another specialist said my thyroid was switching between hypoactive and hyperactive but did not feel my thyroid was "bad" enough to treat.

Over the course of several months, I developed a large painful lymphatic tumor and some swollen lymph nodes. My lymphocytes were three times the normal level. My thyroid became enlarged. I developed high fevers at night with chills, sweating, and violent shivering for six weeks. Another doctor tried to convince me that the insomnia was due to menopause and that the fevers at night were hot flashes. I knew this was not the case. My body temperature registered 101°–102°F at night and 97°–98°F in the morning. I was shivering and would sweat profusely when I broke the fever. During those six weeks, I gauged my night by the number of washcloths I saturated during the night. My health continued to deteriorate. The root cause was never determined.

I have a more holistic philosophy to dealing with health problems and do not believe in treating diseases with toxins. I knew for certain that I did not want to seek any further traditional medical treatment and did not want to start biopsying and treating any "disease." I did not want to limit myself to chasing and treating the symptoms. I rejected the bone biopsy. I decided at that point I did not want to seek a diagnosis. I knew I was seriously ill and I did not want to give the illness any power by labeling it. I knew it would not serve me or my family to label it. I did not want the stigma, sympathy, or worries associated with it. I only wanted to find the cause and eliminate it so I could work on restoring my health.

I came to realize this experience was a necessary part of my journey. I became too sick to function. I had severe fatigue and exhaustion, and I could not think clearly. I was largely out of commission. Other than keeping several commitments per week, I spent four months in bed. I knew at a very deep level that I had to live through this long enough to figure it out and write about it.

I could not figure out what was causing this or what I needed to do to heal. I was feeling a bit defeated because nothing was working. I was losing hope that I would be able to figure this out, and I knew there was a cause that I was missing. I knew if this illness was going to progress, I did not want to opt for surgery or drug treatments. At a core level, I did not believe either of those options would serve me.

My body rejected any supplements. For several months the only thing I could eat was organic applesauce.

Everything else made me feel nauseous. I forced myself to drink water to stay hydrated. I knew I could not assimilate nutrients and my body was not detoxifying. I felt as if I was being poisoned. My life force was slipping away. I surrendered to the possibility that this may be my fate. Every day I lay in bed wondering what was poisoning me. My heart would ache as it raced in my chest, and sometimes I had labored breathing and I wasn't even moving. I had pains in my stomach and my abdomen was distended to the point that I felt miserable. My body twitched in multiple locations simultaneously. I could not think clearly. My vision was deteriorating. My eyes and brain felt like they were burning, and my brain would often feel as if it were floating. I considered my cell phone and my cordless phone my lifelines as I laid in bed suffering from all these afflictions that made no sense to anyone.

While I did turn to traditional medicine to get help in finding the cause of my symptoms, they were unable to come up with any answers that satisfied me. I feel it is necessary to share my journey of how I came through it and learned what I have about its cause.

The Shocking Realization

One day in April 2017 as I was lying in bed going through all of this in my mind, I began to ask for answers. I have always been observant and quite intuitive, but I had no idea what was going on. Why isn't anything helping? Is it too late for any nutrients to help? What does my body need? Why can't I figure this out? What am I missing? What do I need to know? I had been able to solve all of my health challenges in the past. There had to be a higher reason I was experiencing this. I began a conversation with God. Is this my fate? Really? Why am I enduring all this if it is just to die? There had to be more to it, more to do. I was open to being used in service and for a higher purpose, but I had to be able to make sense of it. I couldn't do anything about it if I didn't understand what was happening. I needed an answer. Then out of nowhere, I heard very clearly: "The smart meter."

I believe it was a Divine intervention. I may be discredited for sharing this experience. I realize that it may sound crazy, but in full disclosure, this was my experience. I have had several other experiences with this "inner voice" and it has never steered me in the wrong direction. To this day, I believe I would have died if I hadn't received that "message." It was my fate to know and to act on what I have learned.

My initial response when hearing this message was: "No way. How could this be?" I climbed out of my bed, where I had spent the majority of the last four months, and went downstairs to my computer to search "symptoms caused by smart meter exposure." As I began to read the results, I found that I had 13 of the 15 most commonly reported symptoms related to radiofrequency exposure.

At the time, I had never heard of anyone getting sick from smart meters or radiofrequency. I was shocked, angry, and in that moment, relieved to have something to pursue. I felt my passion coming back. As a scientist, this was a moment of tremendous power. I realized the EMF meter I had used a few years earlier to measure my smart meter when it was installed was not the proper type of meter. That meter was not capable of measuring the radiofrequency pulses that are emitted from a smart meter. I started doing some research online and realized the only way I would be able to investigate this was to invest in a radiofrequency meter with the proper range and a body voltage meter. The meters arrived days later. As I opened the package, I knew these meters were either going to give me the answers I needed to validate my theory or leave me further defeated with no answers or direction on how to solve this. I was hopeful, but I had no idea what I would find.

While I believe I have a pretty good understanding of the energetic field, in full disclosure, I knew next to nothing about electricity or radiofrequencies. It was a learning curve for me to even operate these meters and understand what the readings meant. I took my first body voltage reading in the area of my home where I spent most of my time working over the past several years. My reading was 15.38 volts—an extremely high and shocking level. I thought I must have the scale wrong; it couldn't possibly be 15.38 volts. Upon further study, I realized the meter was correct. How could this be?

A level this high could interfere with many cellular functions. Tears of both terror and joy welled up in my eyes as I realized this invisible force was harming me. I had no idea how to protect myself or remedy the situation, but I now had the answer I needed and was ready to investigate. In that moment, a friend texted me to ask how I was doing, and I quickly responded, "My smart meter is killing me." It was in that moment that I took back my power and decided I was not going to stop until I figured this out.

What I found over the next couple weeks was the radiofrequencies causing this health crisis were not only coming from my smart meter. That meter was a part of the RF levels in my home, and I believe it was the cause of my failing health, but there were several other major contributors in my house. These included my Wi-Fi router, the enabled Wi-Fi on the computers and devices in our house, my cell phone, my family's cell phones, my microwave oven, my smart meter, my neighbors' Wi-Fi and smart meters, my three cordless phones, and the phone base station. The area of my home where I spent the majority of my waking hours is situated in the worst possible location in proximity to all of these sources.

This is not something traditional medicine knows anything about or has any idea how to treat. Nothing taught in medical school prepares doctors to identify this issue, and there is not yet a definitive test or marker in the blood that will lead to a diagnosis. In most cases, it simply goes undiagnosed until it leads to chronic diseases that can be diagnosed and treated without finding the cause. I realized I was pretty much on my own to come to an understanding of what was going on and what I could do to fix it.

One of my doctors who is also a personal friend warned me that people will think I'm crazy. I told him I don't care what people think of me for having EHS. If people choose to ridicule or judge me, that is their issue. My only concern is what people would think of me if they knew I had knowledge and information and didn't do anything about it.

I have found a doctor who understands the impact technology has on my health. We are working together to come up with solutions. He believes I experience chronic inflammatory response syndrome (CIRS) and a problem with histamine degradation. Regardless of how my symptoms are labeled, my body is experiencing a breakdown in its ability to fight and to heal.

I am still learning to manage electro-sensitivity. While our bodies may adapt to this technology over time, I do not believe it will happen in the near future. I will not resign myself to being exposed to radiofrequency to the extent that it continues to poison my body. I am hopeful that the technology will change, that I can adequately shield myself to be able to live in harmony with technology, or my response will be to spend time in remote areas to limit my exposure and give my body time to heal. Either way, I will continue to find better ways to live with this technology until I find a solution. I have dedicated my life to educating others on how to be proactive and protect themselves and future generations.

Lessons from a Radio-Free Retreat

I had spent a lot of time figuring out how to reduce my exposure at home, but I was still using a lot of wireless technology. I realized the only way to really get away from the radiation and test this was to get off the grid. I decided to visit the National Radio Quiet Zone, which is in a remote area of West Virginia and has strict regulations on radiofrequency devices and no cell towers. I spent a week as disconnected as I could while maintaining a somewhat normal lifestyle. I had minimal exposures to RFs that were outside of my control. These included intermittent exposure to Wi-Fi and cordless phones when I went to town, to cars driving passed with smart technology, and from people who leave their cell phones and devices turned on. Even though there are no cell towers there, if a phone or device is left on, it is consistently sending out RF signals searching for a tower.

I noticed significant improvements in my health over the course of the week. My energy level increased and my vision improved. The twitching throughout my body and the leg cramps stopped completely. I found it easy to carry on conversations: I had clearer thoughts and was able to effectively verbalize my words. I did not experience any of the tingling or burning in my head or pressure behind my eyes that had been nearly constant for months. My average resting pulse rate decreased from 125 beats per minute to 74 beats per minute. My average blood pressure decreased from 130/81 to 112/68. I truly felt like myself again.

I had the privilege of meeting and interviewing other electro-sensitive people from around the world who came to this area to seek refuge from RFs. Their stories were eerily similar to mine. Many claim their symptoms began upon the installation of their smart meters. I am not concluding that smart meters are responsible for all of these problems. Perhaps the strong pulses they emit put our overburdened bodies over the edge. I believe the pulsing microwaves from my smart meter triggered my body into a state of EHS.

Each source of EMR has unique frequencies and different pulsations. Not everyone experiences the same symptoms or reacts similarly. Some react only to specific frequencies. Some react only to certain devices and appliances. Some can have Wi-Fi but cannot tolerate cell phones. Some can tolerate specific cell phone carriers but not others. Some cannot tolerate any radiofrequency whatsoever. Most cannot tolerate smart electric meters. Regardless of the type of sensitivities each of these people experience, they are finding the solutions they need to restore their health, stay alive, and get a little peace of mind.

The fact that everyone has different reactions to different exposures makes it nearly impossible to evaluate. Conventional science will have a hard time studying the effect of this on the population and getting repeatable results. It is not likely that we will see independent studies with true control groups. Sadly, most of this technology has been rolled out without ever having been studied for safety to our health.

It was very scary to experience all of these sensations and symptoms in my body before I figured out their cause. Now, it is frustrating, and I feel like a burden to those around me, but at least I am learning to manage it all by reducing my exposure. With radiation blanketing public and private spaces, electromagnetic radiation is nearly impossible to avoid. It has drastically changed the course and quality of my life.

At this point, I do not want to have to move to West Virginia. It is an 11-hour drive and very far removed from "my life." I am happy to know the option exists and feel at some point I may be forced to go there in order to survive. In late 2017, I found a location about three hours from my home that is good for my body and soul. It is a small, hermitage retreat cabin nestled among the bluffs and woods, with no smart meter, Wi-Fi, cell service, or television. Currently, the nearest cell tower is over a mile away. I function best when I go there for three nights once per month. It is not always feasible or possible to do that. It is a place I can go to rejuvenate when my body seems to be failing.

The typical symptoms I now experience when I am exposed to RF radiation include erratic spikes in blood pressure and resting pulse rates, pressure and tingling in the head, pressure behind the eyes with a sensation of my head feeling as if it were floating or about to explode, burning of face and eyes, excessive thirst, severe visual disturbances, shortness of breath, hair loss, skin rashes, fatigue, confusion, forgetfulness, brain fog, fevers, and headaches. These are followed by a couple nights of insomnia, inability to stay asleep, twitching throughout my body in multiple places simultaneously, extreme tightening of the muscles in the neck and shoulders, and foot and leg cramps. I can be relaxed with nothing on my mind and my body goes into panic mode. Once there, I have a difficult time getting out of it.

I also lose my ability to complete a thought and lose my train of thought, and I often stop talking mid-sentence to figure out what I am trying to say. I often say or type the wrong word. For example, if I intend to type "the yellow bird," I might type "the yesterday bird." My brain finds a word that is similar in some way, and I exchange the word between my brain and my mouth or my brain and hands without noticing. I have to really proofread everything I type. It causes me to work slower and requires me to spend even more time on the computer. It is not an easy task to write a book when you have this problem. If I don't catch my typos, people assume I am using an autocorrect feature that is changing my words. I get frustrated with myself because I know my brain is capable of so much more and often feel it is failing.

When I am in a high radiation area, such as near a Wi-Fi router or a digital enhanced cordless telecommunications (DECT) phone, also called a cordless phone, I sometimes develop tremors in my right hand and sometimes my eyeballs twitch.

Despite all my efforts to minimize my exposure, in 2018, I began to experience atypical seizures and absence seizures. These seizures further impact my brain. In some cases, they have caused temporary amnesia, and in others they put me into a catatonic state where I can't talk. My lips and gums begin to burn and feel as if I have eaten a block of salt. I have also become more sensitive to EMFs and have found the seizures are not only triggered by overexposure to RFs but also to certain EMFs and light-emitting devices.

It is a well-accepted fact that the light patterns on televisions and computers can cause seizures for people with epilepsy. It is worth noting that a number of people in forums of the Epilepsy Foundation say their seizures are triggered by wireless radiation.

I had an MRI of my brain to rule out a brain tumor, a carotid Doppler to ensure there were no blockages and that my brain was getting adequate oxygen, and an EEG to measure brain waves. The EEG was abnormal and showed excess brain waves in the right hemisphere of my brain. This makes perfect sense as the left side of my brain seems to be working well when I go into a seizure. The right side of my brain goes into a bizarre state. I had the EEG at the hospital where I used to work. There are multiple antennae on the roof and an abundance of radiofrequency generating equipment. The entire time I had the test, my left side was twitching. Upon leaving the hospital, I had a seizure.

Research shows that brain activity and physiology is altered and that changes occur in the EEG rhythms of 12–30% of those exposed to low-level microwave radiation (Bachmann et al. 2006). Another study showed it is possible to alter the human EEG activity of alpha and beta bands when exposed to ELF EMFs at frequencies corresponding to those same bands (Cvetkovic and Cosic 2009).

According to Dr. Carlos Sosa, MD, there is a simple medical explanation as to why electro-sensitive individuals experience issues with their brain, including seizures. He told me:

There are three basic receptors that have to do with both EHS and multiple chemical sensitivity (MCS): serotonin, histamine, and capsaicin. These receptors are crucial in the physiopathology of the disease because they are the first to become deregulated, and they become "autonomized," that is, the body loses regulatory control over them and they become a part of the autonomic nervous system. There is a cascade reaction in every tissue and organ, and eventually the central nervous system gets involved. Eventually adrenaline, noradrenaline, GABA, and basically all neurotransmitter receptors get involved with the complete failure of brain electrochemistry. When incitants such as chemicals, EMFs, molds, mycotoxins, viruses, and bacteria combine with protein kinase A and C, these are phosphorylated and increase the hypersensitivity by one thousand times. (Dr. Carlos Sosa, MD, email to author, November 7, 2018)

Unfortunately, my body has become so hyper-reactive that I can no longer tolerate much radiation. It seems that my body is on overdrive, locked into a chronic state of fight-or-flight as I also react to certain electromagnetic fields. I can only tolerate short periods of time on my devices, even with my computer on airplane mode and the Wi-Fi turned off and using a wired mouse and keyboard and Ethernet connection. I must wear special glasses in order to use the computer or watch TV or else my brain suffers from dizziness, a swirling sensation, and triggers a seizure response.

I remain committed to living as normal a life as I can for as long as I can. I have no plans of going completely off the grid if I can effectively manage my exposure. I will continue to limit the use of my electronic devices and use them in a much smarter and more cognizant manner. I eliminated my cell phone, cordless phones, Wi-Fi, all wireless devices, and smart meter. I have no smart appliances or smart televisions. I use telephones and the Internet only via wired connections. If I start reacting to RF sources coming in from outside my home, I sleep in an RF-blocking sleeping bag. I wear RF blocking glasses when I go out in public or while sensing radiation exposure. I cover my body in special silver RF blocking fabrics and garments while travelling. I opt out of full-body scanners in airports. The RF blocking fabrics generally set off the metal detectors, so I build in extra time for security interrogations and pat-downs. I shield my car while I drive. I keep a cell phone but only in the event of an emergency while I am on the road. People get frustrated with me because I am hard to reach and often don't get their messages. I have learned to make self-care my priority. These measures have become necessary for my survival. I have learned to adapt, and these actions have become the norm.

EHS seems to come with a continuous downward progression of consequences. No one can predict what you can do about it or what will happen next. I spend much of my doctors' visits educating the medical staff. When I have seizures or other acute response, I don't seek medical help. I know the Wi-Fi and devices in the hospital or medical office will probably make me worse. All my local hospitals have cell towers on the rooftops, smart meters, and numerous wireless devices and remote monitoring equipment. I often find myself with serious medical symptoms such as chest pain, dangerously high blood pressure, fast resting pulse, and a brain that is not working properly, with a sensation of the room spinning and with everything going dark around me. Or I go into a seizure, and I know the only thing I can do at that moment is get myself to a safe position and wait it out.

I feel the effects of my neighbors' smart meters. I contemplate if I should pay to remove my neighbors' smart meters. I look at real estate constantly. When I visit properties, I measure radiation levels and work hard to find a safe way to live. As 5G rolls out, I will have no choice about a transmitter being put on or very near my property. Radiation levels will increase everywhere. It has largely consumed my life. It is expensive to buy the meters, shielding devices, supplements, and supplies. I am constantly buying and testing new gadgets and materials to protect myself. It is difficult for me to work my part-time job in a medical practice because of the Wi-Fi and patients carrying phones. I have cut back to just one day per week, but now I have found I have more seizures on the day following work than any other. When I see clients, I must have them turn off all their devices. I generally can no longer see more than one client per day. I expend a lot of energy helping others. When I give talks, I have to be very careful of my exposure to radiation and usually get overexposed and suffer the consequences for the rest of the day. I fear that my brain will stop working while I am on stage. It is difficult to earn money when you can't function. I plan my life around the radiation. I often go off the grid for a few days prior to giving a talk or making a public appearance. While I normally consider myself to be an optimistic person, I find myself wondering if there will come a day when my brain or body will have had too much. I fear that my brain function may not come back after a seizure. What if I can no longer speak or think clearly? Thankfully, my determination to find a way to live a normal life despite all of this and my will to live and share my journey remains stronger than the EHS.

I am a social person, and I do not like that I must now spend so much time confined to my home in order to stay safe. I feel my freedom has been taken away. It is not that I want to be lazy or reclusive. I am not looking for sympathy. I have done a lot of work on myself and feel I was in a pretty good place prior to all of this. While I have been through a lot, as anyone has, when I turned 50, I had no major medical problems and did not require any medications. I know I may be discredited for writing this book and standing firmly against organizations and industries that are very powerful. I am not doing this for publicity. It is not just another topic to write about. I had four other books planned and started before I was injured by technology. I was very excited about that plan, and felt I was living my purpose. Prior to the installation of my smart meter in 2015, I was working four part-time jobs. I was traveling, speaking, and networking regularly. I like to keep busy and experience life in a meaningful way. I love to share my stories and findings with others. I love to learn, study, and research topics of interest to me. It is my passion and purpose in life. My interactions with others are now largely limited by my ability to control the circumstances and exposure levels.

I believe the current and expanding technology has not yet been proven safe. I believe it has already caused much harm. I feel the best way I can help myself is to learn as much as I can and then help others by sharing what I have learned to hopefully prevent this from happening to them. I see myself as a bridge between the scientific community and the lay person. Getting involved in this movement was not part of my plan. Now it is my mission, and I consider it my life's work.

As far as social implications go, I realized I used to spend a lot more time on my devices and social media than I needed to in order to maintain my connections and interactions with others. It was passing time, but it was not contributing to my life in any meaningful way. I now have more free time to live life in the moment and enjoy others in person. For that reason alone, it is worth disconnecting more regularly. One thing is for certain, when I look around and see everyone focusing their attention on their cell phones, it saddens me. People don't realize how consumed they have become by their phones. I really don't miss my cell phone that I once thought I couldn't live without.

No one knows if the health effects of EMR exposure can be reversed. No one knows the impact of new technologies and what they will do to people who suffer from EHS. No one knows at any point in time when their body will have had too much and they too will become electro-sensitive.

Outsmarting Smart Devices

Prior to figuring out that EMR was the cause of my failing health, I was considering giving up my privilege to drive. I had made several very dangerous moves that could have caused me and others harm. I could not think clearly and found myself really second-guessing my driving. I found I was becoming afraid to make left turns across traffic because I didn't trust my judgment. I had this profound sense of brain fog when I drove. On one occasion, I went through a red light and didn't realize until I got through the intersection. This sense of horror came over me as I realized what I had done. The best way I can describe the sensation in my head when a phone is on in a car is that it is similar to when someone cracks open one car window while you are driving on a highway. There is an annoying and irritating percussion and vibration in your head. You have to open another window to make it stop. In the case where a cell phone causes this sensation, opening a window does not help. My brain feels as if it is heating up. I begin to feel nauseated.

When I began measuring the radiofrequencies coming from these devices, I found the levels they emit are allowed levels. It is "normal" for these devices to emit such levels and these levels are possibly necessary for these devices to work as they do. After becoming mindful and shielding many of my devices, I would measure levels in my home for extended periods of time to find out what type of spikes I would see. One day while away from home, I texted Will and asked him to check the highest level recorded on the radiofrequency meter. He replied to my text that the maximum reading was 250 $\mu W/m^2$ (microwatts per meter squared). Immediately after, he sent another text saying when he sent me that text, he was near the meter, and the meter reading jumped to 1,827,000 $\mu W/m^2$, the upper limit of my meter. This spike came from his sending the text message. Just imagine if you are being exposed to radiation levels thousands of times higher than the highest level in your home each time you sent or received a text message.

In response to this, I switched my cell phone to airplane mode and took it out of airplane mode a few minutes at a time only if I needed to use the phone or check my messages. If I needed to make a call from my cell phone, I used speakerphone. If I was in a place where it is not appropriate to use the speaker, I held my phone several inches from my face. I kept all cell phone calls to a minimum length of no more than a minute or two. If I was going to be on a lengthy call, I used my corded landline phone.

After finding out how high the readings were coming from my cell phone, I began to question if my phone was impacting my driving. Further research gave me a clear understanding that cell phones are constantly looking for towers while you are driving and that is when they give off large spikes of radiation. I confirmed this by taking RF meter measurements while driving with cell phones on and with cell phones off. I now always keep my phone in airplane mode or off. When I am driving others, I ask them to put their phones on airplane mode as well. The brain fog while I am driving is now reduced by about 90–95%.

I am concerned about autonomous cars or those enabled as Wi-Fi hotspots or synced to a cell phone giving off high levels of radiofrequencies. Finding a car with the lowest radiation levels will be my number one criteria when it comes time to buy a new car.

In reducing some of this radiation, I had recaptured my ability enough to think, to critically analyze my symptoms and all of my RF meter readings before and after taking action to reduce my exposure. There is no doubt in my mind that I experience hypersensitivity to radiofrequency exposure or radio wave sickness. Most people do not react as strongly as I do. I am essentially a canary in the coal mine. I have always felt one of my purposes has been to experience things for the benefit of others. I often inadvertently take on illnesses, figure out the causes and preventions, and pass this knowledge on to others. I have an insatiable curiosity to figure things out. It is my nature. I feel confident in saying that radiofrequencies were killing me and are harming many people. I believe they are the cause of many symptoms and mystery illnesses, and over time, they can lead or contribute to diseases such as diabetes, thyroid disorders, heart disease, Alzheimer's disease, anxiety, depression, lymphoma, and leukemia. I have found there are increasing numbers of people around the world who have an electrohypersensitivity.

I am not a doctor or an expert on radiofrequency. I have spent almost two years researching this issue. I know what is true for me. I am willing to be wrong. I accept the consequences of sharing this experience and the results of my investigation. I know I am coming from the heart with the best of intentions to help humanity to thrive. I don't believe it is safe to wait for the industries or government to take action. It is up to us to protect ourselves and our families.

In sharing my story, I hope my wake-up call becomes your wake-up call. We can all take better care of ourselves as a result. I'm still learning about radiofrequencies and ways to shield them at the time of this writing. I believe it is too important of an issue to wait until I fully understand it to warn people to take precautions. It is quite possible that it can take 10, 20, even 30 years for people to develop illnesses from the cumulative effects of the radiation we are exposed to. The truth is, in our modern society there is no way to be completely safe from radiofrequencies. As we learn more, I will post information and resources on our website, www.TormentedByTechnology.com.

Secondhand Radiation Exposure

Radiation from other people's devices is a serious concern. I invest a lot of effort to protect myself. I am often affected by radiation emitted from other people's devices. An example of this is when I am in a restaurant and people are on their phones. Sometimes this causes a burning sensation in my eyes and brain, a rapid temporary deterioration of my vision, a fast pulse, and heart palpitations, or it "turns off" my brain.

I can generally look at my check, calculate the tip, and add it together without thinking twice. When I've been irradiated, I can no longer do this. I stare at the check struggling to figure it out, start counting my money, look back at the check and am so confused. Often the person I am with asks if I am alright or if I have enough money to cover my bill. It is sad.

I previously mentioned the concept of secondhand radiation. I want to get mad at the people around me who are harming me. I feel resentful toward those who, at a restaurant, send messages to other people rather than converse with those they have chosen to dine with or who feel they must check in or post pictures of their food on social media. I must keep reminding myself that they don't know the damage that is being done.

Once you know the potential risks, it is up to you to take responsibility for your choices, behaviors, and usage patterns and to protect yourself and those around you, those who may be sensitive and suffering as a result of your usage, and those who cannot make the decision for themselves, such as children and pets.

Looking Back

After spending nearly two years investigating RFs and EHS, it is clear to me that my symptoms, ranging from severe fatigue to the lymphatic tumor and elevated lymphocytes, matched those that have been reported for decades as symptoms of radio wave sickness. When I look back over my life, a few things stand out that may have been early warnings that my body did not appreciate the electronics I was using.

From 2011 until 2014, I worked in a medical office with my knees up against a computer tower for long periods of time throughout the day. I had knee problems during that time. For the first time in my life, I often had to wear a knee brace. Everyone said, "Once you have knee problems, you will always have them." The computers I used in that office had laser mice. I had consistent pain and tingling in my right wrist and arm. I always operated the mouse in my right hand. In 2015, I left that office to work in a satellite office that is fast-paced with no time to sit down. Almost immediately, both the arm and knee pain stopped. I have been completely free of that pain since. I didn't make the correlation at that time, but considering I had experienced pain for four years and have been pain-free for three years, it feels pretty significant to me.

I also had been diagnosed with trigeminal neuralgia in about 2005. This condition is marked by severe facial pain. I always experienced pain along a branch of the trigeminal nerve that traverses the right side of my face. It was always worse if I used my cell phone or cordless home phone. I held the phone to my right ear. I clearly remember several times while on the phone, telling the person I was talking with that my face was "seizing" and I needed to end the call. Sometimes, I would move the phone to the other side of my face to ease the pain a bit. The other main triggers were X-rays, including airport scanners and digital dental X-rays.

Many people report becoming electro-sensitive immediately following a severe physical trauma. I had three such events.

In 1991, I was working in research and development of aerosol technology. I sustained a head injury resulting from a lab accident. I had hit my head on a cast-iron explosion-proof temperature recording chart. I was knocked out and suffered both a concussion and whiplash. It caused years of headaches, but I never noticed any immediate reaction to electronics.

In 2009, I was electrocuted and required emergency medical care. The point of contact with the source of electricity was my right hand. I experienced pain and jolting sensations up my right arm for several weeks following the incident.

In 2015, just prior to becoming or realizing I was electro-sensitive, I had taken a traumatic fall off the top of a steep flight of stairs in my home. I again was knocked out, suffered multiple injuries, and spent months in physical therapy. I lived my life up until this point with a photographic memory. I never felt right from a neurological standpoint after that accident. Because this event correlates with the time I began experiencing the symptoms of EHS and the time the smart meter was installed on my home, it is quite possible there is a connection between the physical trauma and the EHS or that the fall was a result of the EHS.

It is important to note that I used wireless technology consistently for many years before it severely impacted my health. I had been using a cell phone, cordless phones, and Wi-Fi for more than 20 years.

Some Thoughts on Cures and What Is Helping Me

I like to think outside the box. I have been experimenting with supplements, homeopathic combinations, allergy desensitizing techniques, and various devices that are intended to block radiation, to utilize the earth's natural frequencies, or are designed to create a sort of white noise or static to disrupt the ability of the RF wave to affect the cell.

There are obvious measures that you can take to support your health. It is critical to reduce your toxic load. Eat a healthy diet, eat fresh organic foods, and get plenty of sleep. Stay active and keep your body moving. Do things outside and spend time in nature. It is not always easy for someone who is electro-sensitive to get sleep or spend time outside if they don't have a safe area to spend time in.

I have been experimenting with grounding. Grounding, or earthing, is a practice where you allow your skin to come into contact with the ground so it can absorb free electrons from the earth. It helps neutralize free-radical damage that occurs in your body. Some people I interviewed are using this technique and feeling some benefit. If you want to try grounding, you must be careful. You can do more harm than good. The earth in some areas of North America is highly electrified and you may not properly ground. Be aware of your surroundings. I believe you need an area, preferably in the woods, on a beach, or away from any buildings, where you can stand barefoot on the earth for at least 10 or 20 minutes. Trust your body on this. Try it and see how you feel. I am leery about grounding pads and devices that plug into an outlet because you can effectively become an antenna, pulling the electrical voltage through your body to the ground.

I use Shungite, a black mineraloid, or mineral-like material that is mined in Russia. I carry the stones, and wear a ring and bracelet which are made of Shungite. It feels beneficial to me. I am currently using Schumann resonance frequencies in my home and a static-generating device. I do not feel any of these are the miracle cure, but I feel better with them than I do without.

There are many white noise devices, radiation-disrupting products, chips, diodes, and other products claiming to protect you. I have been experimenting with a number of them. I would urge you to be skeptical of them. There are sham products that make claims that cannot be substantiated. You do not want to get a false sense of security. I lost a dear friend to a brain tumor. He used chips and devices on his cell phone, cordless phone, Wi-Fi router, and computer, all of which he used regularly. If his chips and blocking devices had worked, I don't believe he would have gotten the brain tumor.

Always reduce your exposure as much as possible before testing any products or supplements. There is no evidence at this time to suggest any product or pill can be used to protect you without limiting your exposure.

Products work differently for different people. Trust your gut and pay attention to how you feel when experimenting with any such products.

The Emotional Toll

While I have shared a lot about the physical impact EMR can have on the body, I haven't talked much about the mental stress it causes. I generally consider myself to be strong-willed and do not like to feel sorry for myself. However, the emotional toll is quite devastating. It is stressful to manage life with EHS. There are so many logistics of managing exposure. It comes with a large financial burden and the loss of certain income streams as you can no longer tolerate certain work requirements. For me, the loss of certain aspects of my work has been difficult because I love my work. I enjoy helping people and animals but feel I can no longer serve them at the level I once did.

I feel a sense of grief and loss because my life has had to change so dramatically. My plan for my life has been largely stripped away. Socially, I feel my life has come to a screeching halt. I am also a bit fearful because I don't know how much my body can tolerate and what the future holds. It has forced me to realize that my life may be cut short.

I also feel a strong sense of sadness. Once you fully understand the biological impact of EMR, you know that if we don't change the way we use technology, there will be a lot of people, children, and animals suffering as a result of the decisions made in the name of money. The thought of this makes me angry. The telecom industry is probably the most powerful and profitable of all industries, and yet they can decide to expose all of us to these frequencies regardless of how it is harming us. They have the resources and engineering capabilities to make their technology safer. Instead, they choose to jeopardize the health of the entire planet and refuse to look at any of the research that shows harm or listen to the experts who are trying to warn them.

I have been blessed with a supportive family and a network of friends. I have also diverted some of the emotional turmoil into a passion to spread the word, team up with others, and make a difference. I developed a technique called GetSet tapping, which helps to reduce or release the intensity of negative emotions. I use the technique whenever I feel overwhelmed.

For anyone that considers themself to be electro-sensitive, know that it is important for you to have a way to handle the emotional turmoil. EMR is known to cause anxiety, depression, and sleep disturbances. These conditions can severely affect your emotional well-being. You need a support network, a focused plan for self-care, and a healthy way to manage your stress. You may need professional counseling or medical help.

My Supplementation Protocol

I have been asked to share my personal supplementation protocol. It often changes according to how I feel and if I am experimenting with anything new. My current protocol includes an Nrf2 activator, vitamin C 1000 mg, vitamin D₃ 5,000 IU, B-complex with methylcobalamin instead of cyanocobalamin and niacinamide instead of niacin (niacin causes flushing for me and with the high pulse rate it tends to make me to feel anxious),

Ashwagandha 470 mg, vitamin K2 100 mcg, selenium 100 mcg, and magnesium as L-threonate or in its elemental form. I notice a decline in my cognitive function if I skip the Nrf2 or vitamin C for a few days. I feel I benefit from taking homeopathic remedies. It may not be necessary to take all of these supplements, but for now, I feel better when I am taking them. I believe it is beneficial to take supplements with antioxidants. I recommend taking an antioxidant or better yet, eating a diet rich in antioxidants. It is important because RFs appear to cause significant oxidative stress in the body, which increases free radicals.

Some Thoughts on Melatonin

I will often use a sublingual melatonin spray at night at a dose of about 2 milligrams. There is a lot of scientific and anecdotal evidence that RFs affect one's ability to sleep and alter our melatonin production. When you become low on melatonin, it not only disrupts your sleep cycle but also has other detrimental effects. It is important to most functions and systems in your body that you get adequate sleep. If you get adequate sleep, your body will make melatonin, which seems to be protective against radiation. You may have heard about the blue light phenomena, whereby the blue light emitted from certain devices will affect one's ability to sleep. It is important to turn off your radiofrequency transmitting devices as well as all electronic devices which emit blue light in order to get the sleep your body needs. Your body produces its own melatonin naturally between the hours of about 10 p.m. and 4 a.m. if you are sleeping or resting in total darkness. If you are checking your phone or devices, watching television, have a night-light or electronics with blue or green light in your bedroom at night, you are probably not going to make the melatonin your body needs.

While it is best for your body to make its own melatonin, it is often not possible to sleep for the proper duration when you are under emotional stress, work a swing shift, or are exposed to RF radiation. For some, it makes sense to use a supplement. Be aware that if you take too much melatonin, you may experience vivid nightmares. I have heard conflicting reports on why this happens. It is either from the dose of melatonin itself, or perhaps it puts you into a deeper sleep than you are used to getting, which might lead to the vivid dreams or nightmares. Start with the very lowest dose recommended, or even half of the dose, for the first night. Inform your medical doctor about any supplements you are taking so he or she can ensure there are no known interactions with your medications.

Chapter 7

The Proof Is in the Stories

In this section, we will share some of the stories we obtained through interviewing other people who experience EHS. Some of the people we interviewed wanted to keep their stories confidential. We honor and respect their wishes. Some candidly shared their stories but did not want them in the book. Some told us they were afraid to let others read their stories because they fear that people will think they are crazy. Some are afraid others won't believe they experience the symptoms they do. Others don't want people to know how they live. They are embarrassed by the stigma associated with the condition. It is sad that industry and medicine in most countries deny that this problem exists and that society often discredits those who suffer most. It is with great appreciation that we have been granted permission to share the following personal stories in this book. Each of the following stories is true. In some cases, names were changed in order to protect their anonymity.

The biggest tragedy is that so many of the people we interviewed got seriously ill before they figured out what was causing their health crisis. Many people are being treated for symptoms of various diseases and conditions such as anxiety, depression, thyroid disorders, memory issues, lymphoma, leukemia, skin cancer, brain tumors, diabetes, neurological disorders, headaches, and attention issues. They have no idea that technology may be causing their problems.

The condition of EHS is largely misunderstood. This is because industries tell us there are no concerns with non-thermal effects, funding is not provided to independent organizations or universities to study its effects, medical schools don't teach anything about this, and the medical field does not recognize the symptoms or diagnose EHS. Often patients presenting with EHS are treated for the symptoms they experience or the resulting disease without ever understanding its cause.

Research shows that everyone is affected by RFs at a cellular level. Some people are just better able to tolerate it for the time being. While men seem to suffer as much as women from EHS, the majority of the stories that follow are from women. Many children are suffering as well. Children are presenting with more autoimmune problems, digestive issues, anxiety disorders, and autism than ever before. We have to question the correlation between the rapid increase in the incidence of these conditions and the increasing levels of wireless radiation.

The people in the following stories wanted to come forward and share their stories to help others realize they are not alone. They suffer from varying degrees of symptoms. Some notice subtle changes in their body when they are exposed to EMR. Others have drastic and immediate consequences from their exposure. We are hoping you or someone you know may be able to identify with some of their stories so you can recognize where your symptoms may be coming from, understand the magnitude of this issue, and better understand those who suffer from EHS.

This condition is real. No one we interviewed had ever heard of EHS and did not figure out the cause of their problem until becoming quite ill. Many sought medical help with no success. Many noticed a sharp decline in their health after their smart meters were installed. Often people figured it out as a result of paying close attention to what made them sicker and by trusting their gut feelings. Many were left to experiment on their own to figure out what helped them. For some, the only answer has been to become completely reclusive.

Many of us who are electro-hypersensitive and have been injured by technology have become warriors to fight for our health, well-being, and our lives. It is not an easy task when you can't work in society, you are very sick, your brain is not working, and no one knows how to reverse this or help you. The most emotionally charged question we face is how are we going to survive if technology doesn't evolve into safer infrastructure or frequencies? You can't help but fear that it will only become more difficult as new technologies are introduced and the old manual ways of doing things become obsolete and your only choice will be to become reclusive. Our intention is that by sharing this information, we can become a voice for everyone being affected, and *everyone* is being affected.

It is probable that many of you reading this book are suffering from health effects from EMR exposure and are being treated for other diseases, symptoms, or disorders. We urge everyone to take this message seriously, reduce your exposure, and monitor how your body responds. We hope you gain an appreciation for the magnitude of this problem as you read the following stories. Pay attention to the solutions each of the subjects found as they worked to learn and determine what actions helped them most.

Laura's Story

Laura is the mother of three, a former chemist who works from her home in Los Angeles. In 2008, she added Wi-Fi to her home and also had a smart meter installed. Her health began to deteriorate. She developed intermittent heart palpitations and shortness of breath. She had ringing in her ears. Laura also had frequent migraine headaches. She felt as if her nerves were being continuously zapped. This created a lot of physical and emotional stress.

In 2010, she and her family moved to a new home. She began doing all her work from a computer at home. She sat at a desk with a Wi-Fi router, cordless phone, cordless keyboard, and cordless mouse. She had a smart meter right outside her bedroom window.

She became very ill. She had constant migraines. She couldn't sleep. She felt as if she were being electrocuted all the time. She couldn't stand to live in her own skin. She had complete brain fog and could not put her words together. She felt dizzy and nauseous all the time. Laura felt as if she were being tortured. Along with her heart palpitations, she developed heart pain. She sought medical help. ECGs did not show any heart problems. She became anemic and her blood cells were sticking together. She saw several medical specialists including a hematologist. No one could figure out what was causing these problems.

Laura suffered with all of this for seven years. It became unbearable, and she began to question if life was worth living.

When Wi-Fi was being installed in her children's school, she decided to do some research. She learned that it could cause health effects. She began to reduce the wireless devices in their home. To her surprise, her symptoms began to resolve. As she spent time in areas with more wireless radiation, her symptoms returned.

She is an active volunteer in her children's school but now suffers the consequences of being exposed to the wireless radiation. If she visits someone's home, she often feels sick for several days afterwards. She was a very active and adventurous woman and now feels that she has to think long and hard before doing anything.

Laura has gotten rid of her Wi-Fi, wireless devices, and has had her smart meter removed. She is able to sleep again. Her home is a sanctuary for her and her family. She now works from her home using all wired technology. She feels better but is concerned about the future because there is no way to opt out of 5G and fears that it will make us all sick.

Joe's Story

Joe is in his 50s and an engineer who was living in a very rural area when a smart meter was installed on his home. Shortly after the installation, Joe began having trouble sleeping and severe problems with high blood pressure. He began to question the impact of the meter and proceeded to measure the electrical fields around his home. He demanded that his power company remove the smart meter. Within a day of having the meter removed, all of his symptoms resolved and have not returned. Joe does not have Wi-Fi or cordless phones. He keeps his cell phone off most of the time. He has remediated a lot of the radiation in his home in order to protect his health.

Jane's Story

Jane is retired and living in a suburb of Atlanta. For almost two years, Jane suffered from chronic itching. The itching went across her left shoulder, left breast, and down her left arm to her elbow. It had become quite troublesome for her. She mentioned it to two of her doctors, both of whom had no explanation for it. She also experienced random spikes in her blood pressure that increased as high as 216/111, according to her records. Jane often sat in the same chair while she watched television in the evening. Jane's cordless home phone sat on a high end table a couple feet from her left shoulder. Jane's daughter suspected the phone might be contributing to the itching sensation. She purchased corded landline phones and disconnected Jane's cordless phone system. Jane's itching gradually subsided over the course of two months. She has now been free from the problem for about a year. Her blood pressure is also much less erratic.

Jane notes that sometimes when she has her cell phone near her on her right side, her right arm begins to itch. She is convinced that the phones are the cause of this issue. She does not have any other problems with other devices. She has had her smart meter removed and has worked to reduce the levels of radiation in her home to be proactive about her health.

Derek's Story

Derek is an entrepreneur who lives on the coast in a small California beach town. He began wearing a fitness monitoring bracelet in 2016 to monitor his physical activity and sleep patterns. After wearing the monitor continuously for four months, he began to have issues with high blood pressure. He had extreme anxiety and trouble sleeping. He sought medical help. Over the course of several visits, he was put on medications for blood pressure, anxiety, depression, and sleep. Derek struggled to get the right mix of drugs to correct each of the problems. He also tried several alternative modalities to support his health and get relief from the symptoms. Neither his medical interventions nor hypnotherapy could offer him the relief he was desperately seeking.

In 2017, I suggested Derek remove his fitness monitoring bracelet. After five days, Derek began to feel better. For the first time in several months, he was able to experience restful sleep. He got his blood pressure under control and has gotten off the anxiety, depression, and sleep medications.

Derek continues to use other wireless devices. As a hobbyist photographer, he uses his cell phone to take photographs. He sometimes gets a rash on the hand in which he holds his phone. If he uses his phone for more than an hour, the skin on his hand gets red and flaky, and the skin between his thumb and index finger begins to peel.

Derek is a perfect example of the type of biological affect some people experience from devices. Each device affects everyone in a different way, so it is important to pay attention to your body and trust your gut if you suspect something you are doing is contributing to your symptoms.

Sue's Story

Sue lived most of her life in the suburbs of New York City. As with many who suffer from EHS, Sue first experienced symptoms of chemical sensitivity. This began in the 1990s. She started to have trouble thinking when she was under fluorescent lights. She became ill if she were exposed to synthetic chemicals and fragrances. She became very sick between the years of 2007 and 2010, at which time she discovered her power company had installed a transmitting AMR meter on her family home. She had been noticing that her brain felt "fuzzy" when she was on the phone and had a suspicion that somehow electricity played a role.

Sue's chemical sensitivities had become so severe that she was required to wear a carbon mask to go out in public. She shared that at first it was uncomfortable and she did not want to embarrass her children. An empowering conversation with her daughter helped her to realize that she did not need to compromise her social life or her ability to go out in public wearing the mask just because it made other people feel uncomfortable for a few minutes.

She saw many doctors and was never fully satisfied with their inability to figure out what was causing this. Some put her on antibiotics, which only seemed to fuel the fire as it further disrupted her immune system.

Sue and her husband's bedroom sat next to the wall with the transmitting utility meter, and they had a metal bed with metal springs. She also had a breaker panel in the room below her bedroom. She had been experiencing tremendous fatigue. In 2009, she also discovered that her cell phone made her fingers tingle and her wired computer mouse caused shooting pains and numbness in her arms. She began to feel extreme fatigue when she leaned in toward her computer. Sue began to experience heart arrhythmias and required medication. She also noticed that she would get pain in her forehead when she watched television. She discovered that her sensitivity to chemicals evolved into a hypersensitivity to electronics.

She and her husband hired a building biologist to assess the levels of radiation in their house. They shielded the wall with the transmitting AMR meter and rewired some of the house to reduce the voltage. Sue also moved to another room. As time went on, she continued to get sicker as the technology around her increased. Her neighbor's use of technology would make her sick.

Emotionally, this injury took its toll on Sue and her family. She found that some people didn't believe her; some of her friends distanced themselves from her as she could no longer attend social functions or visit others due to the electronics in their homes. Her family adapted by using technology in strategic ways to avoid increasing levels in the home. Sue found herself celebrating the success of simply walking down the hallway from one room in her home to another without falling. She fought to stay alive.

She became empowered to educate others. She tried to stop Wi-Fi from going into her son's school. She was unsuccessful in stopping the efforts but worked hard to educate her kids and keep them as protected as possible. It helped her to have a sense of purpose. She said those who suffer from EHS are like soldiers. They are strong and determined but are often too sick to fight or go to Washington.

As technology became more advanced and her neighbors began incorporating more technology into their homes, Sue became progressively more ill. Her skin would burn. She and her husband became a united force in getting creative and figuring out the best way for her to survive. They converted a room in their home for her with complete shielding and no electricity. Because of the shielding, it had no light. It became increasingly difficult for her to stay in the room as she felt as if she were in solitary confinement.

In 2015, she began to spend hours in her car. She would take her meter to find places that were safe for her to park. She would often sleep in her car. Even during New York winters, she would sleep with hand warmers and a double layer of sleeping bags. While she had a beautiful home down the block, she was unable to stay there. As she sought to seek refuge in her car, people would sometimes knock on her car windows or call the police on her. She recalls one evening as she drove to her parking spot and found a car parked there, she began to cry.

No one understands the level of hopelessness one feels when they find themselves feeling as if they are running out of options. She spent a tremendous amount of effort trying to explain to others that she was injured. Her words often fell on deaf ears.

In 2015, her community replaced their street lights with LED lighting. At that point, she had nowhere to go. She truly became a refugee. She says she was kicked out of her own life. She and her family had to grieve the life they once lived.

She and her husband decided to visit the National Radio Quiet Zone in Green Bank, West Virginia. They slept in a tent. Sue was finally able to sleep after having suffered sleep disturbances for 10 years.

In 2016, she moved to Green Bank and currently rents while her husband of over 30 years continues to live in their home and work in New York. He drives eight and a half hours to visit her every other weekend. He brings her groceries and supplies to save her from having to go into town, as driving is difficult for her and the electronics and lighting in the stores make her ill. She began meeting others there who validated her condition. They too have come from all over the world to seek refuge from electromagnetic radiation. She was able to embrace her new life and become part of a community again. She feels great while she is there and stays protected from those sources of radiation that affect her. Her husband is happy to have his wife back.

Sue says, "This is a chronic condition, and it is all about how well you can manage it."

Patty's Story

Patty is a school teacher. She lives and works in a large US city. Patty's school is equipped with all the latest in wireless and smart technology. She spends much of her workday in a "smart classroom" with LCD projectors, smart screens, electronic touch boards, Internet, and videoconferencing equipment, much of which can be controlled remotely. For the past several years, Patty has noticed that she frequently gets headaches after working with this equipment.

She became suspicious that some of her health challenges were related to electromagnetic and wireless radiation in 2016. She noticed she was waking up most nights between 2 a.m. and 4 a.m. Once she would awaken, she would have trouble getting back to sleep during that time. Somehow, she instinctively knew it was related to electromagnetic radiation.

In March of 2018, she began having heart palpitations while teaching. She went to her doctor and had an ECG, which did not show any problems or explanation for the palpitations. She continued to experience palpitations at times and had additional ECGs to rule out any heart problems. Patty believes her heart palpitations are related to the smart equipment.

In her home, Patty does not have Wi-Fi. She uses an Ethernet cable for Internet connection and always keeps her laptop in airplane mode. She keeps her printer connected to her laptop via a cable, and because it has wireless printing capabilities, she makes sure she turns it off when she is not printing. She states that the steps she has taken in her home have helped her symptoms.

Over the summer, she is able to teach from home via her computer. She feels much better than when she is in the classroom. Patty continues to explore sources of EMR and works to reduce her exposure whenever possible.

Anne's Story

Anne is retired and living in Southern California. She first began to question the impact electromagnetic radiation was having on her health back in 1985 when she was experiencing strange reactions. This started shortly after she had dental work that involved having metal crowns placed in her mouth. She experienced buzzing, loud ringing noises, and clicking in her ears when she spoke on the phone. Her work at the time required her to spend a lot of time talking on a business landline phone. She believed the metal in her crowns was somehow reacting with the electromagnetic fields or wiring in the phone as she held the phone to her face.

Soon after, she noticed that she would have tinnitus and hear buzzing and clicking noises when she was near high-voltage power lines or utility poles.

As technology advanced over the years, Anne began using a cell phone. Once while she was on the cell phone and walked in front of a refrigerator, she experienced a sharp pain in her head and the tinnitus increased. While she is uncertain as to why this happens, she believes there is a definite correlation between her symptoms and her electromagnetic surroundings.

Anne told me the problem gradually worsened and she has become more sensitive. She also feels her sense of smell has heightened to chemical odors. She cannot tolerate cleaning products or strong fragrances.

Anne began looking for places to live that did not have Wi-Fi or cell towers nearby. She has spent the last three years living in a home in the forest and spends as much time outside as possible. When she goes to a city, she has a difficult time because the tinnitus gets louder and she is not able to tolerate machinery. The sound of a motor operating, such as that of a fan, air conditioner, or refrigerator, is very irritating to her. If she is in a room with a Wi-Fi router, her head and ears become overwhelmed with noises and clicking sounds.

While on a trip in the summer of 2016, something happened that ramped up her problem. She suddenly became highly sensitive. She feels perhaps it was some exposure but is not certain. She notices that when she drives she gets tinnitus and vertigo and it often happens right before she approaches a cell tower. Along with the vertigo, she also experiences issues with her balance and states that it "hits like a wave."

Anne says that many more people seem to be complaining about tinnitus lately, and she feels it is related to the rapidly expanding technology.

She now considers herself to be highly sensitive to electromagnetic radiation and radiofrequency. Anne finds that limiting her time in the city and spending time in nature away from electronics helps her to cope.

Brittney's Story

Brittney is a 24-year-old college student and entrepreneur. She is mindful of her health and wants to eat, sleep, and exercise sensibly. For many years of her life, Brittney has lived a quarter mile from a cell tower. She got her first cell phone when she was 14 and was required to share it with her siblings. She first noticed that she was reacting to her cell phone when she was in high school. She felt very anxious, but only when she talked on her cell phone. She did not understand why this happened.

She developed severe twitching in her right eye that lasted several months. She always held her phone to the right side of her head. She went to her doctor and a specialist, but they were not able to give her an explanation other than perhaps she needed more sleep, since eye twitching can be a sign of sleep deprivation.

She has experienced skin rashes that present as white patches and come and go. She had biopsies, which were inconclusive.

At 21, she realized that her cell phone was causing her a lot of distress. At 22, she was spending a lot of time in a large city. When she was in the city, she developed pains in her legs, which felt like growing pains. She experienced fast heart rates and severe headaches with a squeezing sensation in her head. As a student, she often uses Wi-Fi. She reports having difficulty with concentrating and comprehension, as well as serious brain fog. She gets the sensation that her brain is "not there."

She often wakes up feeling frustrated and fatigued. Sometimes she needs to turn off all of her devices and lay down because her body needs a break from all of it.

When she is on her phone or in an area of higher radiation, she feels absentminded. She feels confusion, lacks concentration, and feels distracted during a conversation. She hears the person but feels as if she is zoning out and needs to ask the person to repeat themselves.

Brittney has other issues which she suspects are related to wireless technologies. She has trouble with sleeping. Sometimes she cannot sleep at all, and at other times, she feels she sleeps excessively. She often feels overheated as if she has a fever. She has taken her temperature, but it is not elevated and is often lower than 98.6°F. The skin on her neck feels as if it is burning. She has frequent stomachaches and digestive issues.

She recently spent several days in a remote forested area with no cell towers or Wi-Fi within range. She reports having a sense of relief, no stomachaches or digestive issues, that her thoughts were coming together, and that she felt clearheaded. She felt this offered a solution to her symptoms and validation to her concerns about technology, but at this point in her life, this is not a practical way for her to live.

In an effort to live amidst all the technology, she now puts her devices in airplane mode whenever possible and completely turns off her computer and Wi-Fi router at night. She feels better when she does this. In addition to reducing her exposure, she feels most resilient when she eats healthy and works out.

She once looked around a restaurant and saw almost everyone on their devices. She felt everyone looked like a bunch of robots. She feels people are losing their social skills and are not interacting with each other in a deeply personal way.

She feels many people are affected, but their symptoms are being masked and treated without knowing the reason for them. She is concerned that new technology is not being tested for how it will affect us before we are exposed. She worries about the long-term consequences on her health and on that of the next generation.

When asked how we can protect children, Brittney said it was up to parents to set limits on electronics. She would urge parents not to give their children access to a cell phone or tablet until they truly need one and never to hand a toddler a cell phone. She suggests toys and puzzles instead. She encourages parents to play with their children outside, read physical books, play board games, build with Legos®, ride bikes, participate in sports, rollerblade, take time in nature, and teach their kids to fish and to think for themselves. You will not only reduce their exposure and dependence on these devices but you will also be giving them the gift of your attention.

Melanie's Story

Melanie is a retired executive who has always lived in a major metropolitan area. Melanie first began to question the impact of technology on her heath when she started having issues with insomnia and getting back to sleep if she awoke during the night. She also experienced numbness and tingling in her fingers and toes. She suffers migraine auras when she is around compact fluorescent light (CFL) bulbs.

When she moved to an upper floor in a high-rise building with many neighbors, smart meters on every floor of the building and views of multiple nearby rooftops with satellite dishes, cell towers, and antennae on them, her symptoms intensified.

Melanie is diligent about doing whatever she can to improve her health and shared several things that make her feel better. She found that using a sound machine and unplugging the cable box in her bedroom before she goes to bed improves the quality of her sleep. While the numbness and tingling in her fingers and toes never goes away completely, she attributes an improvement in the severity and frequency of the numbness and tingling to taking an alpha-lipoic acid supplement. She avoids CFL and LED light bulbs whenever possible and uses incandescent bulbs in her lamps and light fixtures.

She considers moving but does not know a place to go where she will not be impacted. She is otherwise happy and well-adjusted where she is. She has spent her whole life in the city. It is not feasible for her to sell her condo and buy a ranch in Montana or a cabin in the woods. Moving is inconvenient, expensive, and a lot of work. Melanie's dilemma is shared by most people who are experiencing symptoms related to EMR. We have to decide how much of our normal lives we are willing to give up in order to escape high levels of EMR and protect our health, all of this with no guarantee that changes in infrastructure won't result in high levels in the new, "safer" location.

Jennifer's Story

In May 2017, Jennifer had a smart electric meter installed on her home. From the moment she walked in the door, she had a metallic taste in her mouth and felt a pulsating sensation throughout her body as if she were holding onto an electric fence. This sensation was intolerable and made her feel as if she were going through the roof. She couldn't function. She felt as if she was under so much tension, she could barely breathe and would rather die than exist like this. She was exhausted but could not sleep.

Her blood pressure shot up, and her face swelled to the point where she was barely recognizable. Within 48 hours of having the meter installed, she was in the hospital. She had an ECG and had a heart monitor, but there were no answers as to why this was happening. Jennifer knew it was from her smart meter.

She contacted her electric company from the hospital and made arrangements to have the meter removed. After being released from the hospital, she bought a tent because she knew she could not go into her house. Her young daughter was also having unusual emotional issues and acting out of character. She and her daughter slept in the tent in the yard for four nights before the meter was removed.

Jennifer explains that the meter was only on her house for ten days. She has had no symptoms in her house since the meter was removed over one year ago. She is able to use her cell phone with no reaction. She continues to struggle when she is near a smart meter. She reports feeling violated because she is required to pay an opt-out fee to keep the meter off her house even though the meter caused her so much distress.

Amy's Story

Amy is a personal trainer who lives in Minnesota. In 2010, she sustained a head injury, which immediately left her with some very puzzling symptoms. She developed pain behind her ear at the base of her skull when she was around a cell phone. She hears an overpowering buzzing sound and experiences a throbbing sensation in her head when she is near a source of RF radiation. She feels extreme anxiety in the area directly beneath her sternum. She states that she is not an anxious person at all but this anxious feeling is overwhelming. She couldn't sleep. She couldn't concentrate. She noticed the buzzing in her head and that the pain in her head increased when she was around a cell phone.

Her neurologist told her to stay away from cell phones and computers. She didn't understand why he made this suggestion at first, but then she realized how much worse she felt when she was anywhere near a phone. She has had eight years to experiment with this. It has had a huge impact on her life.

Amy has found that when she is in board meetings or Bible study, she often can only tolerate about an hour because even when she asks people to turn off their phones, often someone leaves their phone on. She can't sleep that night, and it generally takes her a full day to recover. She manages her time and her exposure very carefully.

As a personal trainer, she asks that her clients turn off their phones or leave them in their car. Her family knows to keep their phones as far from her as possible, and they have a rule in the house that all phones must go off at dinnertime and remain off until the next morning.

When asked how she copes with electro-sensitivity, Amy says that staying home and getting away from sources of radiation help her the most. She finds that when she is camping and sleeping on the ground, she feels the best. She said all of her symptoms resolve, and she feels fantastic by the first morning of camping in the woods. She also sometimes stands on the ground in a forest near her home to release some of the radiation stress from her body. She feels immediate relief from this practice.

Amy has made other modifications around her home. She shares one common wall with a neighbor. Her master bedroom borders this wall. She can feel when the neighbors use their phones and can no longer sleep in the master bedroom. She and her husband now sleep in another bedroom to distance her from the neighbor's phones. She is also experimenting with other devices, including one from Germany that seems to help.

She says it is difficult when people don't take her seriously. She feels that some people don't believe her. That is a common frustration for those suffering from EHS. Some people find it more important to keep their phone on than to protect the health of those around them who may be suffering because of it.

Arthur's Story

Arthur graduated Phi Beta Kappa from Cornell University with a major in mathematics and minor in physics. Later, he attended medical school at the University of California, Irvine. During his third year of medical school Arthur developed a dental problem. He required numerous X-rays and a root canal treatment that needed to be re-treated three times. One day, after several dozen X-rays from multiple dentists and endodontists, he felt an electric current during an X-ray that traveled from his head to his toes. In that instant, he became electro-sensitive.

The next day, he felt electric currents emanating from every piece of electrical equipment in the hospital. During his medical rotations, he experienced severe pain when he was around electrical equipment.

While working in OB-GYN, he got a pain in his stomach every time he turned on the ultrasound machine to listen to a fetus's heart. On surgery rotation, he had crippling pains in his hips that lasted for days after every surgery he assisted.

He was excused from the operating room on the condition he would write a research paper on a topic of his choice. He chose "The Effects of Radiant Energy on Living Organisms." His research educated him about the health effects of electromagnetic radiation, and he understood that electrocautery machines, used in all surgical procedures, expose surgeons to higher levels of radiofrequency radiation than is permitted in any other profession.

In early 1982 while working in the hospital pediatrics unit, his heart rate dropped to around 45 beats per minute for several weeks. One day, he collapsed on the hospital floor. He had all the symptoms of a heart attack. During the following week, he lost 15 pounds. He knew he could no longer be exposed to all the equipment in the hospital, and he quit medical school to save his life.

He could not walk up a flight of stairs without becoming severely short of breath for hours. He moved into a cabin in the woods in Redwood Country in northwestern California, where he shut off the electricity to his home every night. For the next nine months, he did not know whether he would live or die. Within three years, living in the woods with limited electricity, he completely recovered his health. He subsequently moved back to his home city of New York, where he studied alternative healing methods and became a certified Feldenkrais Practitioner and a certified Rubenfeld Synergist. In addition to having a private practice, he was the main assistant for his teacher, Ilana Rubenfled, in her office in Greenwich Village. In 1990, that office became computerized, and he could no longer work there.

When Omnipoint Communications (now T-Mobile) announced in 1996 that they were bringing digital cell phone service to New York, he organized the Cellular

Phone Task Force to oppose it, an organization that thrives today. The first 600 cell towers were built that fall, and commercial service began on November 14, 1996. Within one week, he was again almost dead. On November 21, he packed his sleeping bag, got on the Long Island Railroad, and left town. He has been a refugee ever since.

He spent the majority of the next 12 years homeless in his car, until he finally found a safe haven in Santa Fe, New Mexico in 2004. He purchased an adobe house there in 2008 and feels normal as long as he does not leave Santa Fe. He explained that there is a geological anomaly there that protects from electromagnetic radiation; the extremely high conductivity of the earth there means that those who live there are well-grounded.

Arthur Firstenberg has worked tirelessly and has devoted his life to protecting our health. He started the oldest and largest organization advocating against wireless technology because of its inherent dangers, and he has run that organization even during the years when he did not have a home. He has been successful in stopping smart meters from being installed in metropolitan areas of New Mexico. He is the president of the Cellular Phone Task Force. He currently is the administrator of the 5G Space Appeal and is working to stop the deployment of 5G on Earth and in space. Thousands of scientists, doctors, researchers, environmental organizations, and others from around the world have signed that appeal, stating that they are in agreement that launching 5G will be devastating to our health and that of our planet. If 5G is deployed, it will increase radiation levels everywhere by 10 to 100 times. If 5G frequencies are broadcast over Earth from satellites, there will be nowhere to run. There will be no way to escape the dangers.

In 2017, Arthur published a comprehensive book about this issue titled *The Invisible Rainbow: A History of Electricity and Life*. It gives the entire history and background, which until now has been missing from the public dialogue.

Arthur explains, "We are electrical beings, and electromagnetic radiation is injurious to all life—all humans, all plants, and all animals, not just a select few. Electrosensitivity is a political term, not a medical term. It is used by those of us who have managed to become aware of what is injuring us—all of us, not just a select few. It is a term that is applied to those of us who insist on the truth although our families, friends, employers, doctors, and others are still in denial."

In Summary

While there are a myriad of symptoms people have shared relating to their exposure to RF radiation, the most common are the following:

- *abdominal pain*
- *anxiety*
- *attention issues*
- *autism*

- *balance problems*
- *blood sugar fluctuations*
- *brain fog*
- *burning sensations*
- *cancer*
- *confusion*
- *cramping*
- *depression*
- *difficulty moving*
- *distended abdomen*
- *dizziness*
- *drowsiness*
- *ear pain*
- *exhaustion*
- *eye pain*
- *facial flushing*
- *fast resting pulse*
- *frequent urinary urges*
- *headaches*
- *heart arrhythmias*
- *high blood pressure*
- *infertility*
- *inflammation*
- *irritability*
- *joint pain*
- *loss of appetite*
- *low blood pressure*
- *memory loss*
- *neurological symptoms*
- *numbness*
- *palpitations*
- *rashes*
- *ringing in the ears*
- *skin problems*
- *sleep disturbances*
- *slow pulse*
- *slurred speech*
- *sweating*
- *thyroid disorders*
- *tingling sensations*
- *tremors*
- *unquenchable thirst*
- *vertigo*
- *visual disturbances*

If you are suffering from some of these symptoms, reduce your radiation exposure. It may help you. Talk to your doctor about it. Be prepared for a response that negates the possibility of RFs causing the problem. Remember, industries and the media reassure us that these devices are safe at non-thermal levels. Medical schools and pharmaceutical companies do not teach that there is a possibility of harm. There are two sides to every story. They listen to the industry that looks at the studies that show no harm. We are looking at studies that show harm. We want you to know the side of the story that no one is talking about. We believe you deserve to know if this is causing harm.

Billions of dollars are made annually by the tech industry and power companies. They would rather not know if their devices are causing harm. If they do know they are causing harm, they do not want you to know it.

We are electro-chemical and electromagnetic beings. Our cell membranes are electrically charged. Every cell in our body communicates with electrical impulses. Many of our body organs and systems, such as our heart, brain, muscles, intestines, and nervous system work on natural electrical impulses. It makes sense that man-made electrical interference will ultimately disrupt these systems over time.

The big question is whether we will be able to adapt to these man-made frequencies during our lifetime. I don't have the answer, but I don't suspect it will be anytime soon. This would mean that people will likely get sicker until the telecommunications industry can come up with a safer solution.

Whether or not you consider yourself to be electro-sensitive, the bottom line is that there are no proven safe levels for any RF exposure. There are no guidelines for safe limits for non-thermal exposures. The guidelines that do exist for thermal levels are outdated and need to be reassessed. It is near impossible to know the levels of radiation you are exposed to on any given day. The levels change every second.

Many scientists agree that EMR poses the single biggest threat to our health. At this point in time, no one knows when their body will reach its limit and become hyper-sensitive, until perhaps it is too late. We must all do what we can to reduce our exposure, for ourselves and those around us.

The stories we have shared in this chapter may be an eye-opener for you. While we only selected the stories of a handful of people we interviewed to go into this book, each story was selected because we felt it was unique. Every person we highlighted was credible and has truly suffered to a varying degree from their symptoms. Each felt strongly that the problems they experienced were caused by electromagnetic radiation. Each one of them gave us their heartfelt story and an honest account of their symptoms and how they have resolved them or cope with them. Many of them work hard to educate others, bring awareness to the issue, and do what they can to create change.

Think about which stories resonated with you. Did any of them get you thinking about a symptom that you might be experiencing? Did any make you wonder if your devices or the sources of EMR you are exposed to might be harming you? Please trust yourself. As you explore the next section of this book, think about which steps you can take to reduce your exposure and the impact of EMR on your body.

Chapter 8

How Can We Be Supportive?

There's no doubt radiofrequency radiation will impact us for the rest of our lives. In order to cope in this technological world, it is crucial that you prioritize your self-care. No one can do this for you better than you can do it for yourself. In this chapter, we offer suggestions for those of you who are electro-sensitive or for those who have someone in your life who is suffering from EHS, such as a family member, friend, or employee. Remember that EHS is marked by the awareness that EMR is the cause of one's health issues. Many people do not realize the cause of their health challenges, and they treat them as isolated symptoms. Once you know the cause, you can be proactive and feel empowered by taking the necessary steps to reduce exposure.

What Can Someone with EHS Do to Survive?

We need to support each other. We need to take precautions even if we are not yet experiencing any symptoms. We are all being affected. We can take precautionary measures to be mindful of how our technology use affects others. It is much like smoking.

As society moves to a place of acceptance and begins to realize the impact this man-made radiation is having on our bodies, it is important to understand several things. For those who are electro-sensitive, you may find people don't believe you. Your doctors may not validate your concerns, you may be labeled as "crazy," your relationships may suffer, your marriage may be tested, and you may find yourself feeling afraid and isolated. When people think you are crazy, they have a hard time taking you seriously. As more of us come to the realization that our bodies are being affected and EHS becomes more widely accepted, we will have a better chance to demand and cause change. It is our hope that by sharing these stories, we gain credibility for those who are suffering.

If you are experiencing symptoms, understand that there are many methods and modalities that can help you. There is not a one-size-fits-all solution to this problem. The most important thing you can do is minimize your exposure and eliminate those sources to which you react. This may require you to do some experimenting and journaling about your symptoms. You must then focus your efforts on self-care and supporting the needs of your mind and body.

In addition to eliminating sources of radiofrequency radiation, you can shield your body or your home. This may require enlisting the help of a professional. Spending time in seclusion is also an option.

Section III focuses on steps you can take to reduce your exposure and protect your health. Consider taking as many of these steps as possible. Listen to your body and trust your gut feelings on what makes you feel better or worse. We hope the suggestions we offer will give you insight and lead to solutions.

How Can You Support Someone With EHS?

For those of you who have someone in your life who is electro-sensitive, realize their condition is fragile. This is real. Take them seriously. Respect their need to be protected. If you don't experience a noticeable reaction to EMR, it is hard to imagine what it would be like for someone who does. Realize that they are often forced into isolation. Don't be offended if they cannot attend social functions. It causes real physical harm to be in those situations. Turn off your devices when you are around them and support them the best you can. Knowledge is crucial. There are ways to manage this.

If you are reading this book because you have someone in your life who is electro-sensitive, we commend you and thank you for doing this.

Some think people with EHS are playing the victim role. In reality, these people are warriors. First of all, they have persisted and figured out what was causing their problems. It is commendable that they were willing to trust their gut feelings and think outside the box when often no one else was able to help. It is difficult to balance the life and people they once knew with the need to protect themselves and stay alive.

Someone with EHS does not know how much their body can take. They live in fear of being exposed to radiofrequency or stepping into situations where they know they will be exposed. It takes a lot of courage for someone to put themselves in a situation that they know will harm them. Once you become electro-sensitive, you can no longer do what you want when you want. It is difficult not to fear the next evolution of technology. Everyone who feels the impact of technology on their bodies is quite concerned about what 5G will do to them and how they will cope if cities go to satellite Wi-Fi services. Each advance in technology complicates our lives and challenges our ability to cope.

Understand this comes down to many very sick, largely misunderstood and discredited people and a group of well-intentioned research scientists from around the world who are working to protect public health and are trying to be heard. At the same time, they are up against regulators, policy-makers and multi-trillion dollar industries with lots of lobbying power who would rather deny the problem exists, discredit those who claim to be harmed, and protect themselves from liability.

How Can an Employer Accommodate Electro-Sensitive Employees?

We must ask ourselves how we can make the workforce safer for our employees. As long as an employer can reasonably accommodate you, they have an obligation to do so.

An employer can take simple steps to protect their employees from some of the radiation. Eliminating wireless devices, hardwiring computers and printers, and eliminating cordless phone systems is a great place to start. These steps alone will reduce the exposure for everyone in your business and may make the workplace more productive. If an employee reports that they are electro-sensitive, you can work with them to give them a sheltered area in which to work. If there is the possibility of allowing an employee to work remotely from their home or a secluded and potentially shielded space in the building, it may offer both of you a great option.

If you are electro-sensitive, it is important to educate your employer. If they don't understand the condition, they cannot help you. Perhaps you can give them this book or another resource as a place to start.

If we don't take precautions and protect our employees, eventually we will have more people needing to drop out of the workforce due to the health implications they experience. This will ultimately hurt businesses and the economy.

SECTION III

What You Can Do to Protect Yourself and Your Family

Our intention in writing this book is not to instill fear. We believe most people do not know there is any risk from electromagnetic radiation and would never go looking for information about its harm. For those who suspect a risk, we realize they probably do not want to take the time to review the science. We have reviewed a lot of research. While we share our experience and offer our findings, we encourage you to do your own research and form your own conclusions. As we stated in the first section of this book, we did not want this book to be a scientific paper. It is written to raise awareness. From what we have found, we believe everyone must take a precautionary approach. It is not worth the risk of hoping we are wrong. We wish we could be wrong on this issue. Until radiofrequency radiation at the levels we are exposed to is proven to be safe, we encourage you to heed the warnings to protect yourself, your loved ones, and future generations.

At this point in time, our key strategy to mitigate damage is to reduce exposure. We have done our best to offer as many suggestions as possible for reducing your exposure. We realize that the information that follows can be daunting.

If you are suffering from physical symptoms, we urge you to take as many of the following precautions as possible. If you turn off your Wi-Fi router and remove your smart meter but are sleeping with your cell phone or have a cordless phone in your home, chances are you won't notice much difference. Consider taking a two-week wireless retreat in your home. Take as many of the following actions as possible to reduce your exposure and see how you feel. Move your sleeping location if you must to be as far from sources of wireless radiation as possible. Unplug all cordless phones and Wi-Fi. Keep your cell phone as far from you as possible and keep it on airplane mode as much as you can. Make certain everyone in your home follows the same rules. Finding ways that make you feel better may help you understand the triggers and resolve your symptoms.

If you aren't having any symptoms, go through the lists in the following chapters and pick a few simple actions steps you can take to reduce your exposure. You will likely benefit if you take no other action than these three simple steps:

- *Turn off your Wi-Fi router and the Wi-Fi and Bluetooth features on your mobile devices, as well as put your devices in airplane mode, before going to sleep. If you have a landline phone, let select people know to call the landline in the event they need to reach you.*

- *Unplug and remove any DECT cordless phones in your home.*
- *If you don't yet have a smart meter on your home, opt out. If you can have it removed, replace it with an analog meter.*

Remember, our wireless radiation exposure is cumulative. If you dismiss this because you aren't currently noticing any problems, you may regret it down the road.

Chapter 9

How to Reduce Your Risk

According to some building biologists, any levels of RFR above 10 µW/m^2 cause considerable concern. While there is no truly safe level, experts suggest you should not sleep in an area with an RF reading over 5 µW/m^2. For those who are electro-sensitive, this level may be too high. It is critical to your health that you reduce your exposure while you sleep. While you sleep, your body works to heal and restore itself. That said, this section should help you draw on and implement some of the most valuable tips to reduce your RF exposure and live a healthier life.

If you live near a cell tower, you need to take extra precautions and may need to hire a professional. We've taken consistently high readings in people's homes that were several hundred feet away from a tower. Readings are consistently in the range of 300–500 µW/m^2 with all phones and Wi-Fi turned off. Studies suggest that living near a cell tower increases your risk of RF related symptoms (Saravanamuttu et al. 2016; Abdel-Rassoul et al. 2007).

For comparison, the background level in our home is about 2 $\mu W/m^2$ with everything that produces radiofrequency turned off or eliminated. Even with our smart electric meter removed, we get random spikes that we assume are from the pulsing of our neighbors' smart meters in the range of 1,000–44,000 $\mu W/m^2$. A smart meter can transmit data thousands of times per day causing random spikes at harmful levels. We usually see a few spikes every minute. To protect yourself from these harmful spikes while you are in your home, you may need to hire a qualified professional to shield your home and mitigate any dirty electricity that may be generated by the meter. Be aware that your power company will likely tell you that your meter will only be transmitting for a few minutes per day. This may be true, but they don't tell you that your meter is communicating with your neighbors' meters in the form of thousands of microsecond bursts throughout the course of a 24-hour period.

When we had the cordless DECT phones and base charging station in our home, our background readings throughout the house were in the range of 300 $\mu W/m^2$. The levels near the base were extremely high. The cordless phone generated the same level of radiation as that of living near a cell tower. If you spend a lot of time talking on the phone, we urge you to get or keep a landline phone, to just be sure all of your phones are corded.

Within a four-mile radius of our house, there are 58 cell towers and 377 RF-emitting antennae. Large cell phone masts and towers are easy to spot. There are new cell antennae and transmitters being installed on light posts, telephone poles, traffic signals, and commercial buildings as part of a distributed antenna system (DAS) to increase bandwidth and prepare for faster cellular service.

Many cell towers are large and unsightly. In some areas, cell towers are being disguised as palm trees, spruce trees, and cacti. Some are constructed to look like a crucifix on top of a church steeple. In some cases, the antennae are small and are hidden in plain sight.

These antennae emit strong signals for cellular, paging, and other radio services. Antennae can be placed on towers with multiple transmitters or can stand alone and be placed on top of offices, condos, hotels, churches, light poles, signs, and scoreboards; within elevator shafts; and in buildings. Stand alone antennae are small and difficult to spot as they are easily hidden or camouflaged. Many go unnoticed, and it is not until you start looking around for them that you notice how ubiquitous they are.

Local municipalities have little say over where towers are placed. The Telecommunications Act of 1996 gave jurisdiction over placement of radiofrequency transmitting devices to the federal government. In particular, Section 704 of the Act states that, "No State or local government or instrumentality thereof may regulate the placement, construction, and modification of personal wireless service facilities on the basis of the environmental effects of radio frequency emissions to the extent that such facilities comply with the Commission's regulations concerning such emissions" (Federal Communications Commission 2015).

It will take a long time to undo this infrastructure. It might take years for engineers in the industry to figure out a way to replace it with safer technology that meets the demand for innovation, speed, and convenience. While it is not easy to control what goes on outside of our homes, we can control the amount of radiofrequency we generate within our homes.

Most of the measurements we have taken show the majority of the radiation in a home comes from within the building. The exception may be if you live near a transmitting cell tower or antennae or have smart meters. These sources tend to have a significant impact on the radiation inside your home. Depending on the proximity of your house to your neighbors' houses, you are probably getting radiation from their wireless devices.

Tips To Reduce Your Radiofrequency Exposure

The following suggestions can help reduce the levels of radiation in your home and workplace. These suggestions are based on our experiences. In order to know your levels, you either need to have the proper equipment and expertise, or hire someone who is qualified to do this work. If you borrow or purchase a meter, be certain it has the proper range to measure what you need to measure. We have convenient resources on our website to assist you. Taking the following precautions may help even if you do not have the equipment to measure the levels on your own. These precautionary steps require minimal effort and often have no cost. The majority of the effort comes from changing your normal practices and habits.

Keep your cell phone and wireless devices in airplane mode with the Wi-Fi and Bluetooth turned off whenever possible. While it is in airplane mode, you will not be able to send or receive calls or text messages or use the Internet. Other features of your phone such as the clock, calculator, voice recorder, camera, and alarms will work while it is in airplane mode.

Many gas, electric, and water utilities are transitioning to smart meters. We have had our smart electric meter removed. We are charged a monthly fee of about $22. We do have a smart water meter on our home. It does not transmit unless the readers are in the area. They have a device that transmits to each meter and wakes it up, triggering it to send the data to the reader. They read the meters once per quarter. We have not been able to detect or measure any RF radiation coming from this meter. For those reasons, we have agreed to keep this meter in place. Check with your utility companies to find out if your meters are transmitting. We have an analog gas meter on our home.

Ask your electric provider not to install a smart meter on your home. Some municipalities will charge to remove the meter and will charge a monthly service fee if you opt out of a smart meter and use an analog meter or non-transmitting digital meter instead. Be sure the analog or digital meter that is used in its place does not emit radiofrequencies. Some replacement electric meters have a chip in them and will still remotely send data to the carrier. Ask your electric provider to put in writing that the device does not have any transmitting technology.

If you rent your home or cannot avoid the smart meter, you can buy a shield or supplies to make your own smart meter shield from aluminum screening, duct tape, and a copper wire. If you are not comfortable doing this, have a qualified person do this for you. This will create a Faraday cage and reduce the radiation that broadcasts out the front and the sides of the meter. This is helpful if you spend time in your yard or garden. This may also be protective for your pets, neighbors, and the vegetation on your property. This will only reduce the radiation; it will not eliminate it. You may consider measuring the output before and after putting the smart meter shield in place. The smart meter will still be able to transmit your information to your neighbors' meters and to a collector so it will be sent to your utility company. If your neighbors' meters point toward your house, consider asking your neighbors to shield their meters as well. To reduce some of the radiation from a smart meter inside your home, it will be necessary to put shielding between your smart meter and the areas where you spend time in your home.

Even if you are not experiencing any symptoms from your exposure to radiofrequencies, your body is still impacted. Technology will only continue to expand, and as our devices and appliances become "smarter" and faster, our exposure will increase. Over time, we believe everyone will develop symptoms to varying degrees. The time to take precautions is not after you have advanced disease processes in your body. The time to act is now. It is easier to prevent a problem than to treat it.

Most people don't have the time to do their own research. There have been many studies done on RFs. It is often difficult to understand all the scientific jargon and to weed out the industry bias. Based on the measurements we have taken, these are some precautionary actions you can take to reduce your RF exposure and protect yourself and your family:

- *Get rid of any cordless landline DECT phones in your house. These cause very high levels of RFs, and this is one of the easiest changes to make. Replace them with corded phones.*

- *Keep your cell phone and wireless devices on airplane mode as often as possible.*
- *If you must use a cell phone, connect it to a router via an Ethernet cord and adaptor while you are home. Be sure to get the proper adaptor for your phone.*
- *All phones in your car should be on airplane mode unless you need one for directions. Consider using physical maps or printing directions at home prior to getting in the car.*
- *Keep your cell phone and devices away from your body. Set your phone on a surface and use a stylus.*
- *Use speakerphone when possible.*
- *Use an airtube headset or hollow tube earbuds to keep a safer distance between you and your phone.*
- *Limit the number and length of calls from your cell phones and Bluetooth devices.*
- *If you have a pacemaker, do not use a cordless phone or store a cell phone in your pocket.*
- *Do not sleep with any cordless or Wi-Fi enabled devices in your bedroom or sleeping area.*
- *Do not use fitness monitoring bracelets.*
- *Avoid wearable devices that transmit wirelessly.*

- *If you have a wireless printer, unplug it when you are not printing. It probably continuously transmits even if you have it hardwired.*
- *Avoid wireless keyboards and computer mice. If you must use them, turn them off when they are not in use.*
- *Keep all of these devices as far away from you as possible when you are not using them.*
- *Do not hold laptops on your lap. Use them on a desk or table.*
- *Keep cell phones and tablets from young children. Radiofrequencies are more dangerous to their developing bodies and brains.*
- *Do not use a wireless baby monitor in your home. If you must use one, keep it as far as possible from your baby's crib or children's beds. Place a shield between the monitor and your baby's sleeping area.*
- *Read real books in place of electronic books. If you must use an electronic reader, download the book and read it on airplane mode with the Wi-Fi turned off.*
- *Opt out of having a smart meter on your home or use a smart meter shield. If you already have a smart meter, demand that it be removed. Be aware that you may be charged to remove it.*
- *Ask to shield your neighbors' smart meters if they face your home.*

- *Do not use smart thermostats.*
- *Used wired gaming systems.*
- *Unplug television streaming devices and game systems when they are not in use. Many of them transmit wirelessly even if you do not use them in that capacity.*
- *Opt for analog home appliances over smart appliances. Smart appliances send signals that continuously try to communicate with your smart electric meter, even if you have an analog meter.*
- *Turn off the Wi-Fi on your computer and keep it in airplane mode whenever possible. Use Ethernet cables to connect to your router. Minimize the time you are connected to your wireless network.*
- *Turn off your Wi-Fi router when you are sleeping. If you need to keep it on to keep your phones or alarm system working, keep the router and devices as far from you as possible.*
- *Turn off your Wi-Fi when you are not home to protect your pets.*
- *Opt out of full-body airport scanners.*
- *Consider shielding any devices that emit RF radiation.*
- *Do not live near a cell tower. If you must, adequately shield your home.*

Each of these is one small step in the right direction to reduce your exposure to the many frequencies of RF. As you implement these small changes into your life, you may notice changes in your health. The good news is that we have shared this information with a number of people who have taken some of these preventive measures to reduce exposure. We have received great feedback from them. In some cases, their health issues or mystery symptoms have resolved or improved. It is your responsibility to be proactive about your health.

Tips To Reduce Body Voltage and EMF Exposure

Both ELF-EMF and RF radiation put stress on the body, cause biological effects, and raise body voltage by creating an electric current in the body. In an effort to understand what sort of things increase body voltage, we took measurements all around our house and other people's houses as well as measured people's body voltage. We also loaned our meters to several others who took measurements in their homes and workplaces. Body voltage is consistently higher when the person is in areas of high EMF or RF radiation. Taking just a couple steps away from those areas will significantly reduce body voltage. It is important to note that distance is your friend. The best thing you can do is distance yourself from those things that raise your voltage, even if it is just by a few extra inches.

To illustrate, we measured the RFs, EMFs, and body voltage while Susan was working on her laptop. Her body voltage decreased simply by taking the following actions:

- *Moving the laptop about six inches farther away from her on the table.*
- *Moving the power cord away from her feet and legs.*
- *Switching the laptop to battery power only.*
- *Turning off the Wi-Fi on the computer and putting it in airplane mode. Note that when on a website, listening to a webinar replay, or watching a video, we have found that once it is fully loaded, you can turn off the Wi-Fi or unplug your Ethernet cord and continue to read, listen, or watch as long as you don't change pages while you are disconnected from your wireless network. You can also download your files and then use them while you are offline.*
- *Taking hands off the keyboard whenever reading from the computer. Note that you can zoom to make the text a little larger and move the laptop even farther away. You can purchase a USB keyboard so you can type with the laptop farther away. You can also use a wired mouse with a tracking ball. Use an Ethernet cable to connect your computer directly to your modem so you can use the Internet without Wi-Fi. Use a USB ground cord if your computer plug does not have the third prong.*

It may seem like a lot of effort, but it is simply a matter of being mindful. Taking a few small steps may reduce your risk significantly. Most of us have come to enjoy the benefits of not needing everything to be attached to wires. These changes take a little getting used to. They are soon integrated into your life and become the norm.

Be aware of what is on the other side of the wall where you spend the most time. EMFs and RFs pass easily through walls and floors. Rearrange furniture in your home and workspace so you are at a safer distance from things such as breaker boxes, fuse panels, refrigerators, air conditioning units, and other devices or industrial equipment that may give off large amounts of dirty electricity or electromagnetic radiation.

Here are some additional steps you can take to reduce your body voltage and EMF exposure:

- *Take the precautionary actions to reduce RF exposure as stated previously.*
- *Avoid fluorescent light fixtures. If you have them in your home, we suggest investing to replace them. If they are in your workspace and you have natural light, can you turn the lights off and have enough light to work or add a desk lamp? In some cases, the lights are on multiple banks and you can turn half of them off.*
- *Avoid fluorescent and compact fluorescent lamp (CFL) lights. In addition to putting off high levels of EMFs and high frequency radiation that is absorbed by your body, they contain mercury, which causes a serious threat to the environment that far outweighs the*

benefit of being energy-efficient. Some people feel ill when they are under fluorescent lights.

- *Avoid LED light bulbs. They contain lead, arsenic, and heavy metals. They also emit high levels of EMFs. Use incandescent bulbs when possible. Full spectrum light bulbs are good alternatives but are more expensive.*
- *Replace dimmer switches with standard light switches.*
- *Organize power cords so they are not near your body. Run power cords behind your desk instead of near your feet.*
- *Do not sleep with an electric blanket or mattress pad. If you must use one to warm your bed, turn it off and unplug it before you go to bed.*
- *Unplug electronic devices when not in use. This also reduces your electrical consumption, your electric bill, and reduces your carbon footprint.*
- *Consider using filters in your house which reduce high frequency spikes on the electrical wiring in your home. We use Stetzerizer® filters in our home.*
- *Consider hiring an expert in the field, especially if you or someone in your household is experiencing symptoms of EHS.*

RFs and EMFs pose serious threats to our well-being. Our exposures are cumulative. Chronic exposure to and increasing levels of RFs and EMFs will catch up with us over time. It will serve you to implement these tips to reduce exposure.

Chapter 10

Make Your Sleep Space Your Sanctuary

Your body repairs, heals, and rejuvenates while you sleep. In its innate wisdom, your body has the capacity to undo a lot of the damage that was done during the day from dietary toxins and environmental exposures. You would probably agree that your body would not detoxify very well if you had an IV of corn syrup going into your arm as you slept. While corn syrup is considered safe enough to eat and it is in most of our processed food supply, it is not a food that will promote health. It is genetically modified, and it is a highly refined form of sugar. Your body would work hard to detoxify and process the corn syrup that was going into your body and would not be able to expend its energy on healing. Most of us never consider the fact that we don't give our body a break from technology. Our body will have a hard time undoing much of the cellular damage that is done during the day from Wi-Fi and cell towers, poor diet, and pollution if we sleep a few feet away from our cell phone or in a high field of electromagnetic radiation.

There is no doubt that the electrification of the world has impacted our health. You want a sleep space that is conducive to healing. Consider the placement of your bed in relationship to what is on the opposite side of the wall and what is in the ceiling of the room beneath you.

Think about the placement of your electronics in your home. If you use an alarm clock, where is it? Is it inches away from your head? Can you move it to the far side of the nightstand or perhaps across the room? If it is near your bed, where does the cord run? If it runs behind your bed to an outlet near your head, is there another outlet you can plug into that is farther from your bed? If you must have items plugged in at close proximity to your bed, unplug them before you go to sleep.

Always be mindful of what is on the opposite wall closest to your body, and most importantly, to your head. Is there a plasma or smart TV, computer, refrigerator, furnace, or if you are near an outside wall, perhaps a smart meter or air conditioner condenser unit very near? If you have a breaker panel or fuse box in your bedroom, move your furniture so you do not spend a lot of time near it. Perhaps put a dresser against that wall so you do not sleep or sit for long periods in close proximity to the panel.

Unless you were around during the construction of your home or workplace, have the blueprints or wiring diagram of your home, or have an electrician to help you, you may need to get creative and experiment with moving your bedroom furniture around.

Think about how the wiring might be laid out within the walls. It may run vertically or horizontally from the outlets, switches, and fixtures.

Ultimately, you can simply switch off the breakers supplying all power to your bedrooms at night. You could also have a switch installed in a convenient location in the house to turn off the breaker without having to access the breaker panel. Just be sure there are no critical electronics on the same circuit breaker. Use a flashlight if you need to get up during the night. To reiterate, if you turn off one or multiple breakers, be certain that there is not a pertinent piece of equipment on the same circuit, such as a submersible pump, hot water heater, refrigerator, furnace, or alarm clock.

You can always test some of these steps out and see how you feel. It may be necessary to have a building biologist evaluate your home to see if you would benefit from doing this. Be aware that magnetic fields can still emanate from your wiring with the breaker switched off.

Since our smart electric meter has been removed and our electrical wiring is shielded because it runs through conduit, we find it most beneficial to keep our breakers on, and we use Stetzerizer® filters to reduce dirty electricity on our lines.

If it is not feasible to turn off a breaker and you do not have a meter or someone to assess the electromagnetic levels in your bedroom, you can assume there are significant levels of EMFs coming from the wiring in your walls. Consider moving your bed away from walls with electrical outlets, switches, or strong sources of EMFs coming from the other side of the wall. Ultimately, it is possible that none of the four sides of the bed would be touching a wall.

It may look awkward to have your bed moved away from the wall, but this is about nurturing your body and protecting your sacred sleeping space. In some cases, you can position your bed diagonally in a corner of the room. In this position, none of the sides of the bed are against a wall and only two corners of the bed come close to a wall. This alone will often put anyone in the bed at a safer distance from the wiring. If you cannot move the bed, consider moving the head of the bed away from the wall. This may mean you would be sleeping "upside down" in your bed. Your head will be at the foot of the bed and farther away from a wall. It is probably safer to expose your feet to higher electromagnetic fields than your head.

We realize this may seem very strange. Anyone who suffers from being in close proximity to dirty electricity or a high electromagnetic field knows what a difference changing your position can make.

If you are not experiencing any health issues and feel perfectly healthy, you may not need to take drastic measures in your room. Remember this is about protecting your health, no matter where you are on the spectrum. Take any steps you feel comfortable taking to reduce unnecessary exposure. At a very minimum, move your bed away from any wall that has your home's main power supply or a breaker box on it or directly on the other side of the wall. Be sure to take these precautions for your children's rooms as well. If you have a baby, consider placing the crib away from the walls.

To protect yourself from radiofrequency at night, turn off all wireless devices before you go to bed. If you normally silence your phone at night, you may as well put it on airplane mode. Turn off Wi-Fi routers, modems, wireless printers, and Bluetooth devices, and unplug all cordless phones. You may consider putting your Wi-Fi router on a timer so you don't forget to shut it off. For instance, you can set it to turn off every night around the time you get ready for bed. You can set it to come back on at the time you normally start using it the next day.

You can buy a simple switch that plugs into an outlet if the router is in a location that is not easy to access, or you can buy a power strip. If your router must be on, you can often connect your devices via Ethernet cords and shield your router with specialty fabrics or signal cages. See the resource page on our website for links to such materials and devices.

If you must keep your cell phone on when you sleep, consider hard wiring your cell phone. There are adaptors for many phones that allow you to connect to your Wi-Fi router via an Ethernet cord. If you can't do this, turn up the volume and keep it as far away from you as possible. Consider keeping your phone in an adjoining bathroom if you can hear it from your bedroom.

Chapter 11

Using Nature to Your Advantage

RFs travel through wood, brick, cement block, concrete, drywall, insulation, nylon screening, rubber and asphalt roofing materials, and vinyl siding. They easily penetrate most building structures. If they didn't, your cell phone would not work in your house or while inside a public building. When you try to connect to Wi-Fi, you would not see your neighbors' Wi-Fi networks if your building materials blocked radiation.

Have you ever noticed if you have used a cell phone while driving that you might drop a call while driving through an area of dense tree cover? This is because the leaves of the trees absorb microwaves, much the same way as our bodies do. The signal has a hard time passing through leaves. While this raises concerns about the impact of all the electromagnetic radiation on our trees, it can be used to your advantage.

A house that is surrounded by trees will be more protected from outside sources than one that is not. Be aware that the microwaves travel through wood and likewise travel right through tree trunks and branches. If you live in an area with deciduous trees which lose their leaves in the fall, you lose your protection during the seasons in which the trees have no leaves. Evergreens and conifers on the other hand, keep their needles year round. These offer a continuous level of protection and can reduce the RFR that is coming from outside your home.

If you live in a zone where your trees and bushes do not lose their leaves, use this information to plant trees or bushes so that vegetation protects key areas of your home. If you live in a zone where your trees lose their leaves for the winter, consider strategically planting a few evergreens to block radiation that may be coming from sources outside your home. For instance, if you have removed your smart meter but your neighbors have smart meters and you live in close proximity with a small amount of space between your homes, you can plant an arborvitae or something in the evergreen family that has a small diameter but grows tall. You can plant a "wall" of them to block more of the radiation. Get creative to come up with ways to protect yourself.

Depending on where the source of radiation is coming from, the earth can also effectively block radio waves. If you live in a valley or have rolling hills, bluffs, or mountains around you, you will be more protected. Of course, if there is a cell tower on top of the hill and you can follow a straight line to it, you are not going to have protection from the hills. If you have a direct line of site to a cell tower, you are probably receiving radiation from that tower. As a rule of thumb, the closer you are, the more radiation you receive. A home that is nestled among hills could be a better option than one that is on flat land.

Some people who are extremely electro-sensitive find earthen homes to be quite protective. Of course, living in a cave is not conducive to modern life, but in some cases, extreme measures are necessary to protect your health until you can find a safer way to live and until technology becomes safer.

If you are planning a move, this is the perfect time to ensure you remain as healthy as possible. Take all of this into consideration when selecting a home. Pay particular attention to the proximity of the house or apartment to cell towers and smart meters. If there are major sources of radiation that are outside of your control, you may want to look elsewhere. The health implications and costs of electrosmog remediation are as important as those for mold, asbestos, or radon gas.

For those of you who have become severely electro-sensitive, a thorough remediation of the EMR in your home or moving is often the only option. Be sure to consult with a knowledgeable person when planning your move or hire a building biologist to inspect a home before you commit to renting or buying it. You can even put a contingency in your rental agreement or offer to purchase that the house must pass an inspection for electromagnetic radiation.

Chapter 12

Pregnancy, Children, and RFR

Carrying a baby and having a child is a great honor and blessing. It also comes with tremendous responsibility to nurture that child the best way you can. The gestational use of wireless devices and exposure to man-made frequencies poses questions on the lifelong consequences to your child. Special precautions should be taken by pregnant women to protect their unborn babies (Petitdant et al. 2018). There are also numerous studies which show RFR causes DNA damage (Akdag et al. 2018; D'Silva et al. 2017; Gandhi et al. 2015; Ibitayo et al. 2017; Sun et al. 2017). If there is a possibility that you may want to have children at some point in your life, now is the time to protect yourself. It is important to keep in mind that when a baby girl is born, she has cells for all of the egg follicles that she will ever have in her body. If she experiences genetic damage at any point in her life, she can potentially pass these mutations down to her offspring and to generations to come.

Studies show that wireless radiation may negatively impact sperm viability, mobility, and motility (Gorpinchenko et al. 2014; Pandey et al. 2017; Dasdag et al. 2015). It can also cause testicular damage and negatively affect the male reproductive system (Bilgici et al. 2018). These issues can decrease fertility.

A joint statement signed by over 200 physicians and scientists warns of the risk that wireless radiation poses during pregnancy and urges pregnant women to limit their exposures (The Baby Safe Project 2017).

Dr. Dietrich Klinghardt has found that radiation is concentrated in the womb and that pregnant women need to take precautionary measures to protect themselves and their unborn babies. Children and pregnant women have more water content in their bodies. Water is a conductor and absorbs more microwaves.

A UCLA study found that babies exposed prenatally to wireless radiation have a higher risk for behavior problems and hyperactivity (Divan et al. 2008).

Martha Herbert, MD, PhD , said, "While we aggressively investigate the links between autism disorders and wireless technologies, we should minimize wireless and EMF exposures for people with autism disorders, children of all ages, people planning a baby, and during pregnancy" (quoted in Carpenter 2013).

Children are more susceptible to wireless radiation because their nervous system is developing, their brain tissue is more conductive, RFs penetrate deeper into their head because of its smaller size, and they have longer lifetime exposures (Belpomme et al. 2018).

According to California Department of Public Health Director and State Public Health Officer Dr. Karen Smith, "Children's brains develop through the teenage years and may be more affected by cell phone use. Parents should consider reducing the time their children use cell phones and encourage them to turn the devices off at night" (California Department of Public Health 2017).

In a letter to the Federal Communications Commission (FCC) in 2013, the American Academy of Pediatrics (AAP) issued a statement which said, "Current FCC standards do not account for the unique vulnerability and use patterns specific to pregnant women and children." The AAP "supports the reassessment of radiation standards for cell phones and other wireless products and the adoption of standards that are protective of children and reflect current use patterns" (Electromagnetic Radiation Safety 2013).

There is growing evidence on the detrimental effects of RF radiation on children and adolescents. Studies have shown that thyroid function, adrenal hormones, glucose levels, and melatonin levels can be disrupted in adolescents based on their exposure to wireless radiation (Sangün et al. 2015; Masoumi et al. 2018).

What Parents Must Know

Russia has set limits on radiation broadcasts in schools and urges pregnant women not to use cell phones. France has banned Wi-Fi from nursery schools and requires elementary schools to turn off the Wi-Fi when not in use. Countries such as India and Finland have issued warnings for children using cell phones. France, Italy, Austria, Bulgaria, Poland, China, Switzerland, Germany, Spain, and Israel are among countries taking steps to reduce wireless radiation exposure on children (Parents for Safe Technology, n.d.).

If you have children, please protect them. Children have never been exposed to the levels of wireless radiation that they are being exposed to today. Such levels of radiation have never been proven safe. Our children are essentially guinea pigs. They are exposed from the first moments of life. No one knows what the health implications will be as the years pass. As with anything that has been proven harmful only after many years of use, it is considered at first to be safe, and after decades of denial and cover-up, the truth becomes well known.

There is no harm in taking precautions. If you are pregnant, limit your use of wireless devices and consider shielding your belly with a protective garment. Make your body a true sanctuary to nurture and protect your developing baby. Use the tips throughout this section to reduce the wireless radiation in your home. Make your home a sanctuary for your children.

Parents must think twice about using a phone around their children or about handing their child a cell phone or wireless device for entertainment. If it is connected to a cellular service, or if the Wi-Fi or Bluetooth is enabled, or if it is not in airplane mode, there is a good chance they will be exposed to levels of RF radiation which have been found to cause harm. Remember, a safe level of RF exposure for children has not been established.

You generally can't control how much radiation is emitted in the outside world or in public places, but you can control the amount of radiation you allow in the vicinity of your child. This is the easiest and perhaps most critical decision you can make on behalf of your child.

Chapter 13

How Can We Make Our Schools Safer?

Some countries are taking a precautionary approach. Israel banned Wi-Fi from preschools and kindergarten and places usage guidelines on schools. India has banned mobile cell masts from schools, hospitals, and playgrounds because this type of radiation is considered hazardous to life. In 2015, France banned or restricted Wi-Fi in schools based on the age range of the students (Parents for Safe Technology, n.d.).

If you are a parent of school children, find out what is going on at your children's schools. If they have cell towers near the school and Wi-Fi or wireless technology in the classrooms, be an active part of the solution.

Cell towers near school property means children can have thousands of times higher RF exposures in school environments than existed 20–30 years ago (BioInitiative Working Group 2012). The explosive use of technology in school has amplified the exposure children receive. In many schools, Wi-Fi is broadcast throughout the building for the entire day, children are provided tablets and notebook computers with wireless Internet connections, and classrooms have smart technology. Demand safer technology in the classroom. Go to the teacher, the administration, and the school board members with your concerns.

It is important to understand that most people do not believe there is a threat to health or well-being because we are told it is only harmful at levels that heat tissue. They may think you are paranoid and that your fears are unfounded.

If you are a teacher or school administrator and cannot get your school board to recognize the importance of this issue, know that you can make rules in your classroom to protect yourself and the students in your room. If devices are allowed in the classroom, teach your students to use technology responsibly. Teach them to turn off the Wi-Fi and put their devices on airplane mode when not in use or at least while they are in your classroom.

Many teachers are women of childbearing age. Some "time" the birth of their baby to coincide with their summer break. They spend most of the school year irradiating their eggs and their fetus because they are bombarded with wireless radiation all day at school.

Request wired connections instead of wireless. If you can't do that, think outside the box. If it is possible, have your school install switches in the classroom to switch the Wi-Fi off when it is not needed. Can you unplug the Wi-Fi in your classroom when it is not needed? If you are a teacher, think carefully about your options.

The schools of the future may need to have radiation-free zones, just as they have peanut-free zones or as public places have non-smoking areas. Many schools in various countries around the world are using wired technology exclusively. They have heeded the warnings and do not offer wireless computers or printers within their school systems.

Studies have shown than RF radiation can reduce IQ, memory performance, and the ability to recall information (Schoeni et al. 2015; Foerster et al. 2018). All of which can in turn lower test scores. We have a family member who was instrumental in keeping cell towers from going on top of a number of schools using the argument that the test scores will be reduced. Sadly, standardized testing is often the way schools are rated, and if there is a way for a school to boost student performance on these tests, the school will sometimes get on board.

Many schools receive substantial amounts of money for having cell towers on the outskirts of their playgrounds and athletic fields, or having antennae on their rooftops or other structures such as cooling towers and chimneys. Consider the possibility that these cell transmitters are accounting for many health issues, mental and emotional challenges, and cancer clusters for the students. If your child's school sits under a cell tower or has constant Wi-Fi exposure or uses wireless devices exclusively and the school administration is not willing to take precautions, consider the option of switching schools or homeschooling. Homeschooling is a viable option that offers many benefits. Curriculum plans are readily available, making it much easier for parents. There is also the option of co-teaching with other parents in your community.

An option to protect your children while in school would be to have them wear shielded clothing. Shielded clothing is expensive and generally loses some of its protective qualities the more it is laundered. In order to launder less and preserve the protective quality of the garments, one could wear the garment over their undergarments and wear clothing over it. For example, a child could wear protective boxers, shorts, or leggings over their underwear and then wear their pants, shorts, or skirt, over the garment. This would protect their reproductive systems while being exposed to radiofrequencies in the school.

As parents and educators, we have the ethical responsibility to protect our children. Many of us protect our children from harmful chemicals, unhealthy food, and secondhand smoke, but have we considered their exposure to ubiquitous, secondhand radiation? If there is any risk that six hours of Wi-Fi per day may cause infertility, do we want to wait 20 years and hope that our children are able to bear children?

Chapter 14

Metals Can Be a Cause for Concern

Think about how a microwave oven cooks food. The radio waves excite the water and fat molecules in the food. These molecules vibrate and generate the heat to cook the food. The microwave oven doesn't actually heat the food. The radio waves cause the food to cook itself. If you have ever accidentally or unknowingly put a metal utensil or a piece of aluminum foil in the microwave oven, you will see sparks flying. This is because the radio waves build up and reflect off the metal. Unless we live in a very remote area or without wireless technology, there are probably radio waves all around you. When metals are irradiated by radio waves, there is the possibility that they hold a charge that is released over time. Be mindful of metals in your environment, especially if you are EHS.

Metals Worn on the Body

Think about the metal jewelry that you are wearing. There is some concern that metal frame eye glasses may concentrate radiofrequency. Some report getting headaches when they use a cell phone if they are wearing metal rim glasses or earrings. Underwire bras may carry a charge when you carry a cell phone in your bra or in your purse, which hangs under your arm very near the underwire. Be aware of the metal you wear on your body and pay attention to how it feels, both on and off. Some notice they feel better without metal jewelry, glasses, or underwire bras. It is all about making informed choices. You don't have to get rid of everything you own. Be mindful when you shop. Can you get plastic frame glasses next time you replace your glasses? Can you buy non-underwire or plastic underwire bras instead of metal wires? Perhaps you can wear strung beaded jewelry instead of metal chains. If you wear a watch, can you use a leather wristband instead of a metal one? Or try going without the watch for a week. If you have a prosthetic, metal implant, or pacemaker, do not put your cell phone in your pocket. Reduce the radiation in your environment. If you are electro-sensitive, making some of these changes immediately may be warranted. Trust your body and your gut feelings. Pay attention to what makes you feel better and worse.

Metals in Your Environment

Consider the possibility that other metals could cause issues. Think about ways you can reduce your time in contact with metal. Since we spend the most time in the same place at night, focusing on your bedroom is key. Think about the metals you may have in your bedroom. For instance, you may have metal in your bed frame, headboard, or box spring or have metal inner springs or coils in your mattress. Perhaps you have a metal lamp next to your bed. Do you sit at a metal desk or a table with metal legs? Think outside the box in all areas of your life. How can you make safer choices? Can you replace a metal frame bed with a wooden one? Can you sit on wooden or composite lawn chairs instead of metal ones? Keep these things in mind while you shop.

Dental Connections

Metals in the body and mouth can cause concern. Medical doctors in some countries consider your dental health to be at the foundation of your physical health. Dental infections, sensitivities to dental materials, and currents created by metals in the mouth may be adding to your toxic load and damaging your health. This can make you more susceptible to chemicals and radiofrequencies.

Dental fillings, metal crowns, bridges, orthodontic braces, and implants are possible sources of metal in your mouth. Dental work is quite expensive and generally unpleasant. It may not be essential for you to have all of your dental work redone. Use this information going forward to be proactive when you need dental work. If you are electro-sensitive, dental materials can be a cause for serious concern. It may be necessary to consult with a knowledgeable dentist who understands the issue of radiofrequency and its potential to cause currents on other metals. This is not something the average dentist will understand. You will need to do some research.

One study found higher nickel release in the saliva of people who use a cell phone and have orthodontic braces (Mohammad et al. 2018). This raises concern for those sensitive to nickel because it will increase the level of nickel in their body. It also brings up the question of the possibility that RFR may cause other metals to leach from dental materials such as amalgam fillings and crown materials.

Susan found a holistic dentist who was open to understanding her condition. She traveled out of state to have extensive dental work done. This included extracting all root canal treated teeth, removing a tooth with a metal crown (this crown could have been replaced with a zirconium or porcelain crown, but since it was a back tooth that wouldn't need to be replaced, it was less expensive and made sense to just have the tooth removed), and cleaning up four infections in the jaw bone. She felt this was necessary for her to eliminate some of the metals and reduce her toxic burden, and that cleaning up some of the chronic infection in her system and reducing inflammation could assist her body in healing.

Chapter 15

Thoughts to Consider

U p to this point, we have presented many suggestions for reducing your EMR exposure so that you can protect your health and that of future generations. We realize that taking some of these actions may seem drastic. It is important to note that the sicker you are, the more important it is to take immediate action to reduce as much of your exposure as possible. Treating a disease or medicating your symptoms will not work forever if you don't eliminate the cause of the problem.

Our intention for this book is to give you as many ideas as possible to assist you in remediating some of the radiation to which you are exposed. In this chapter, we provide some thoughts to consider as they relate to the social and environmental implications of technology. We also provide a few additional tips that may help you in some way.

Social Implications

As a society, we have learned to not only live with technology and use the devices to our benefit, but also have begun to depend on them. We have become enslaved to technology. There is a new term being used which addresses this issue of dependence on our devices to do things for us. Digital dementia is the state where you are unable to do certain things without the assistance of technology. Many simply rely on the calculator function to do simple math. You see people take out their phones in restaurants to divide a check in half. Schools are getting away from teaching children to read analog clocks because everyone solely reads the time off a digital display. Many rely on GPS and couldn't read a map if there was a treasure at the other end. Many people no longer know their family members' phone numbers because they rely on their contacts lists. Some schools are getting away from teaching cursive handwriting because everything is typed on a keypad or keyboard. Maybe some of these skills are no longer necessary at a time when technology seems to have taken over the world, but to most middle-aged folks or senior citizens, it is hard to imagine living in a world where simple computations, telling time, or finding a friend's house require an electronic device. We are losing some competence in our society.

In a society where we seem to always need to be connected, we do not even realize how disconnected we have become. If you look around in public places, you see many people who are out with others and connected to their devices. In an effort to maintain their social connections on their phone, they are being antisocial by not interacting with those they are with. It is apparent that many are dependent on and perhaps addicted to their devices. According to *Psychology Today*, problems with media addiction can begin at much earlier ages than many parents realize (Vitelli 2017).

Carbon Footprint

All communication devices require electricity to power or charge. Towers and transmitters require huge amounts of electricity, which increases the pollution generated by the electrical consumption. Giant data servers use massive amounts of energy. They have exponentially increased our carbon footprint. Not to mention the environmental cost of deploying thousands of satellites.

Physical Considerations

This book has focused on the physical harm being done to our cells and our bodies by the electromagnetic radiation emitted from our technology. There are also negative impacts to our posture and the physical structure of our bodies. Many people have their heads leaning forward constantly as a result of looking down at devices. We might also ask ourselves what are the implications of the explosive screen time we are spending on our devices. Simply being on our devices is changing the way we experience life. There are also the physical impacts to our body from the blue light. This is affecting our eyesight, our ability to make melatonin, and our ability to get restful sleep.

Grounding

We previously discussed grounding in Chapter 6. If you are electro-sensitive, it is probably best that you don't use grounding mats or grounding sheets. You can test the effect of grounding in your area by simply standing barefoot outside on the ground. Use caution to avoid areas near buried plumbing or electrical wiring. Pay close attention to how you feel before and after. For some, this simple practice provides relief.

If spending some time standing on the earth seems to give you relief, you might consider taking a weekend camping trip. Be sure to sleep in your sleeping bag on the ground. Do not sleep on a rubber or foam pad. Experiment and see how you feel.

Microwaves and Water

According to the FCC, "Radiofrequency radiation, especially at microwave frequencies, can transfer energy to water molecules" (Federal Communications Commission 2015). This is why microwave ovens heat food and why cell phones can heat up your skin, fat cells, and brain tissue. This is one reason why RFs accumulate in the amniotic fluid and why children seem to be more impacted. It is also quite likely that those who carry more water in their bodies, and even those who have more fluid on the brain, can be more susceptible.

This also brings up the concern that there may be implications of having microwave cell towers on top of municipal water towers. This could potentially be restructuring the water molecules or changing them in some way. This concern warrants further study by an objective source. We have to question the things that are not being studied.

How to Test if Your Microwave Oven Leaks Radiofrequency Radiation

If the RFs generated at 2.4 GHz in your microwave oven can cause the food inside to cook, what does the radiation that escapes do to you? We have yet to find a microwave that does not leak. In our home, we measure extremely high levels of microwave radiation in the entire kitchen while the microwave oven is in use. No one should be in the room if the microwave is running. It is best not to use a microwave oven. When you cook with it, it destroys the nutrients in the food, and if it is not sealed, it irradiates everyone within a certain radius while it is running. It is very clear to see what is happening when you own the appropriate meters. We own five such meters in different ranges because for us it is necessary to gain the appropriate knowledge to write this book, and for Susan, it is essential to her quality of life. These meters can be expensive and complicated. Not everyone is able to invest in one. If at all possible, we suggest investing in a simple combination meter that has indicator lights on it. Such a meter is easy to operate and can be purchased for under $200.

If you don't have access to a meter, a simple test you can perform is to place your cell phone in your microwave while the phone is on. Place the phone face up in the microwave oven. Do *not* turn on the microwave oven. Simply close the door. Then from another phone, call your cell phone. If your microwave oven is completely sealed and shielded to prevent radiation from getting out while you are cooking, it will not let microwaves in either. If your phone lights up or receives the call, then you know microwave radiation can penetrate the oven seal.

Chapter 16

Moving Forward

Electromagnetic radiation is wreaking havoc on all forms of life. The magnitude of the problem is beyond most of our comprehension. We suspect many people reading this are trying to understand how this can be happening. Many trust their elected officials, regulatory agencies, and industries to protect us. Some may think this is a conspiracy theory. While no one knows for certain how they will be affected, we know that everyone is affected. Unless you take action to reduce your exposure and demand safer technology, you will likely fall sick or decline in health as you continue to be bombarded by more radiation and more frequencies. We urge everyone to stay informed and review the research. Ignoring the problem will not make the dangers of electromagnetic radiation go away. It will make it worse. The harm to life on this planet may reach a point where there is no way to reverse the damage. Standing up for yourself and for others is the right thing to do. By failing to take this problem seriously, you are allowing yourself and all other life forms to be bathed in destructive frequencies.

Advancing Technologies

It is irresponsible to roll out the fifth generation of cell phone technology, 5G, without studying the effects of all the frequencies and modulations that come with it. These should be studied not only on humans but also on animals, plants, and insects such as bees. The environmental impact and the human toll may prove catastrophic. A safe level should be agreed upon by independent scientists and doctors that have no financial interests or conflicts of interest before it is broadcasted on every living thing.

This technology uses millimeter waves (MMW). These MMWs don't travel well over long distances or through many materials that other frequencies easily penetrate. For these reasons, the infrastructure will have to be broadened and will entail many transmitters placed in close proximately. While no one knows for sure what this will look like, it will probably mean at least one transmitter on every block. This can mean that the transmitter may be put up right in front of your house, broadcasting continuously over your property. The main health concern with the MMWs is that they are absorbed by the first few millimeters of the skin, causing possible heating of those tissues at high exposure levels (Wu et al. 2015). This thermal effect may lead to damage of the eyes and skin.

The affect of MMWs on humans has not been well studied. The combination of all the different bands of RF radiation we will be exposed to simultaneously has not been studied for human safety. It is assumed that if nothing heats the human skin, meaning it does not have a thermal effect, then it is safe. Even if a 5G device is not near the body, 5G frequencies have the potential to heat human skin. The 5G technology will be inescapable. It is hundreds of times more powerful than anything we have been exposed to. The antenna infrastructure will be massive. You will have no control over where the antennae will go. There could be an antenna placed on a pole or a sign on or near your property. The thought of frequencies being broadcast down from satellites to blanket the entire Earth is horrifying.

It is pitched as helping the consumer to increase download capacity and streaming capabilities. In reality, it will keep everything connected in one global surveillance system in the smart grid. I am all for intelligence which protects us from terrorism and malicious threats. The smart grid will provide massive amounts of information about you to someone. Say you are on your way to the pet store to buy dog food. Is it really necessary for *someone* to know, in that particular moment, that you are driving your car, the speed at which you are driving, if you are wearing a seatbelt, whether or not you are taking your medication as prescribed, what you have in your refrigerator, if someone in your home is taking a shower, how much money you have in the bank, how much money you owe on your credit cards, and when the last time you vacuumed your house?

Is it really necessary to have everything censored, microchipped, and tracked? All of this new technology and infrastructure will not give us as much benefit as it will provide information about us to *someone* else. Study it and form your own conclusions before you buy into the hype. There are security issues because there is no way to know who has access to your private information, who might hack into it, or what can be done with it. You never consented to giving this information away. Once you give up your privacy, it is not so easy to get back. Giving up all of our private information is not as alarming as the impact this will have on our health. Having everything connected wirelessly on this smart grid will require very powerful transmission speeds and expose us to unprecedented levels of high frequency MMW radiofrequency radiation. Keep in mind there are no safety standards that address the long-term chronic exposure to any of these frequencies. I personally do not believe I will survive more than a year or two at these levels. Consider the impact this will have on your health and those you love.

One day, you become overexposed. You develop symptoms and eventually can no longer cope. There are huge public health implications to consider because of the massive deployment of these technologies. If there is even a small percentage of the population who will die from this, don't we deserve to know before it is deployed? The cost of treating all of the disease will far outweigh the profits being generated.

Putting This in Context

It feels very unfair that so many people are currently suffering and struggling to find a way to live. We shouldn't have to choose between living the life we have built for ourselves with our families and social circles, and a life of isolation.

What does the future look like? Might there be cities or radio-free zones that can be sanctuaries for those suffering from EHS, for those looking to be proactive about their health or simply wanting to get away from the smart grid? Ideally, we need to establish these safe zones in every country and state. We need safe places for people to live until we can find a safer way to supply technology to the masses.

We are all for technological advances and the conveniences that computers and devices have brought into our world. We want safer systems and to be appropriately warned of dangers. Many people are exposing themselves to extraordinarily high levels of radiation because they don't know there is a threat. We believe they deserve to be warned before it is too late. It is much easier to prevent disease than to undo disease. It is time to sound the alarm. Let's all work to keep each other safer.

Until we can make a blanket statement about what we have to do to overcome this or negate the effect of the frequencies on our bodies, we must remember that we are here to live our unique journey. We have tremendous power to influence how we experience our lives and our health.

We have the right and obligation to protect ourselves and those who cannot protect themselves. There are often cell towers or antennae, smart meters, and Wi-Fi on the property of most day care centers, schools, hospitals, rehabilitation centers, and nursing homes. Perhaps we are overexposing the most vulnerable members of our population. Most people do not know or believe there is potential risk to their health and well-being. The truth is these frequencies are killing us. A large percentage, perhaps 10%, of the population is already suffering. If technology were safe, there would not be so many people suffering from EHS. If we don't act on this information now, it will be too late. Everyone will eventually be tormented by technology.

Become an Activist

Get politically active. Contact your government officials, leaders, state and federal representatives, members of parliament, senators, governors, and congress people.

Urge them to demand proof that the levels of EMR we are exposed to are safe and to vote against expanding technologies until they are proven safe by independent scientists.

Call your representative. If you know someone who can get you in to speak with them for even 5 or 10 minutes, tell them your concerns. It will make a difference. Let them know that you want them to fight for you and to demand that independent scientists and doctors determine a safe level of radiation exposure before we are subjected to it. A standard reflecting an agreed upon safe radiation level currently does not exist. Go to their rallies and fundraisers. Your vote matters to them. Let them know that you will vote for whoever agrees to fight for this. None of the other political issues, policies, or promises will matter when so many people in the world are suffering or dying because of this.

Share the information with others in your community. Stay informed. Stay positive and focused on finding solutions. Get active by contacting local and national groups to tell your story and express your concerns. Be active in demanding safer schools, workplaces, and public spaces. Spread the word. There are many active groups working to promote safe technology, stop smart meters, halt 5G, and make our schools safer. They are led by experts. You don't have to know the science. Join forces with them. Reach out to them to see how you can help. Be an active part of the solution.

If you can help us, and if this information we have shared has triggered you in any way, please assist us by spreading the word. Buy a copy of this book and donate it to your local schools and libraries. No one can do anything about this issue unless they know about it.

The more people who know and care about it, the better chance we have of keeping everyone safer. We must come together, work together, and leverage our resources.

If one person refuses a smart meter, the utility company writes them off as crazy. If 10% of their customers refuse a smart meter, we get their attention.

If enough people refuse to buy into the 5G hype and tell their carriers they will not upgrade their phone or use the 5G band because these frequencies have never been tested for safety and research shows they harm out health, perhaps they will listen.

When they realize they will not be making tons of money off us, perhaps they will listen.

When the telecommunications industry realizes people know the risks and hold them accountable and liable for the damage they are causing, perhaps they will listen.

As Margaret Mead once said, "Never doubt that a small group of thoughtful, committed citizens can change the world. Indeed, it is the only thing that ever has."

SUGGESTED WEBSITES

Here are sites we recommend for more information—databases of scientific research, action steps you can take, or opportunities to get involved. These sites were active and working at the time of this publication. Visit the resources tab on our website, www.TormentedByTechnology.com, for up-to-date resources and to claim your free gift.

5GAppeal.eu

5GInformation.net

5G SpaceAppeal.org

BabySafeProject.org

BioInitiative.org

c4st.org

EHTrust.org

EMF-portal.org/en

EMFScientist.org

ParentsForSafeTechnology.org

PowerWatch.org.UK

SaferEMR.com

TakeBackYourPower.net

REFERENCES

Abdel-Rassoul, G., O. Abou El-Fateh, M. Abou Salem, A. Michael, F.Farahat, M. El Batanouny, and E. Salem. 2007. "Neurobehavioral Effects among Inhabitants around Mobile Phone Base Stations." *NeuroToxicology* 28 (2): 434–40. doi: 10.1016/j.neuro.2006.07.012.

Akdag, Mehmet, Suleyman Dasdag, Fazile Canturk, and Mehmet Zulkuf Akdag. 2018. "Exposure to Non-ionizing Electromagnetic Fields Emitted from Mobile Phones Induced DNA Damage in Human Ear Canal Hair Follicle Cells." *Electromagnetic Biology Medicine* 37 (2): 1–10. doi: 10.1080/15368378.2018.1463246.

Bachmann, Maie, Jaanus Lass, Jaan Kalda, Maksim Säkki, Ruth Tomson, Viiu Tuulik, and Hiie Hinrikus. 2006. "Integration of Differences in EEG Analysis Reveals Changes in Human EEG Caused by Microwave." *2006 Conference of the IEEE Engineering in Medicine and Biology Society* 1: 1597–600. doi: 10.1109/IEMBS.2006.259234.

Balmori, Alfonso. 2015. "Anthropogenic Radiofrequency Electromagnetic Fields as an Emerging Threat to Wildlife Orientation." *The Science of the Total Environment* 518-19 (Jun 15): 58–60. doi: 10.1016/j.scitotenv.2015.02.077.

Belpomme, Dominique, Lennart Hardell, Igor Belyaev, Ernesto Burgio, and David O. Carpenter. 2018. "Thermal and Non-thermal Health Effects of Low Intensity Non-ionizing Radiation: An International Perspective." *Environmental Pollution* 242 (Part A): 643–58. doi: 10.1016/j.envpol.2018.07.019.

Bilgici, Berşen, Seda Gun, Bahattin Avci, Ayşegül Akar, and Begum Korunur Engiz. 2018. "What Is Adverse Effect of Wireless Local Area Network, Using 2.45 GHz on the Reproductive System?" *International Journal of Radiation Biology* July 2018: 1–25.
doi: 10.1080/09553002.2018.1503430.

BioInitiative Working Group. 2012. "BioInitiative Report: A Rationale for Biologically-based Exposure Standards for Low-Intensity Electromagnetic Radiation." Last modified December 2012. www.BioInitiative.org.

California Department of Public Health. 2017. "CDPH Issues Guidelines on How to Reduce Exposure to Radio Frequency Energy from Cell Phones." Last modified December 22, 2017.
https://www.cdph.ca.gov/Programs/OPA/Pages/NR1 7-086.aspx.

Carpenter, David. 2013. "BioInitiative Press Release: BioInitiative 2012 Report Issues New Warnings on Wireless and EMF." January 7, 2013.
http://www.bioinitiative.org/media/press-releases/.

Cucurachi, S., W. L. M. Tamis, M. G. Vijver, W. J. G. M. Peijnenburg, J. F. B. Bolte, and G. R. de Snoo. 2013. "A Review of the Ecological Effects of Radiofrequency Electromagnetic Fields (RF-EMF)." *Environment International* 51 (January): 116–40. doi: 10.1016/j.envint.2012.10.009.

Cvetkovic, Dean and Irena Cosic. 2009. "Alterations of Human Electroencephalographic Activity Caused by Multiple Extremely Low Frequency Magnetic Field Exposures." *Medical & Biological Engineering & Computing* 47 (10): 1063–73. doi: 10.1007/s11517-009-0525-1.

D'Silva, Mary H., Rijied Thompson Swer, J. Anbalagan, and Bhargavan Rajesh. 2017. "Effect of Radiofrequency Radiation Emitted from 2G and 3G Cell Phone on Developing Liver of Chick Embryo - A Comparative Study." *Journal of Clinical and Diagnostic Research* 11 (7): AC05–AC09. doi: 10.7860/JCDR/2017/26360.10275.

Dasdag, Suleyman, Muzaffer Taş, Mehmet Zulkuf Akdag, and Korkut Yegin. 2015. "Effect of Long-Term Exposure of 2.4 GHz Radiofrequency Radiation Emitted from Wi-Fi Equipment on Testes Functions." *Journal Electromagnetic Biology and Medicine* 34 (1): 37–42. doi: 10.3109/15368378.2013.869752.

Davis, Devra. 2017 "Cell Phone Radiation Health Risks and Recommendations To Reduce Exposure." YouTube video, 2:43. December 19, 2107. https://youtu.be/soii0UUUlwk.

Demasi, Maryanne. 2016. "Mobile Phones and Brain Cancer: 'No Evidence of Health Risk' Not the Same as Safe." *The Guardian*. February 15, 2016   . https://www.theguardian.com/commentisfree/2016 /feb/16/the-debate-about-mobile-phones-brain-cancer-and-artificial-electrosmog-its-complicated.

Divan, Hozefa A., Leeka Kheifets, Carsten Obel, and Jørn Olsen. 2008. "Prenatal and Postnatal Exposure to Cell Phone Use and Behavioral Problems in Children." *Epidemiology* 19 (4): 523–29. doi: 10.1097/EDE.0b013e318175dd47.

Electromagnetic Radiation Safety. 2013. "American Academy of Pediatrics: Protect Children from Cell Phone & Wireless Radiation." September 12, 2103. https://www.saferemr.com/2013/09/american-academy-of-pediatrics-demands.html.

Elwood, JM. 2012. "Microwaves in the Cold War: The Moscow Embassy Study and Its Interpretation: Review of a Retrospective Cohort Study." *Environmental Health* 11: 85. doi: 10.1186/1476-069X-11-85.

EMFscientist.org. 2015. "International EMF Scientist Appeal." EMF Scientist Appeal. Last modified August 30, 2018. https://emfscientist.org/index.php/emf-scientist-appeal.

Falcioni, L., L. Bua, E. Tibaldi, M. Lauriola, L. De Angelis, F. Gnudi, D. Mandrioli, M. Manservigi, F. Manservisl, I. Manzoli, I. Menghetti, R. Montella, S. Panzacchi, D. Sgargi, V. Strollo, A. Vornoli, and F. Belpoggi. 2018. "Report of Final Results Regarding Brain and Heart Tumors in Sprague-Dawley Rats Exposed from Prenatal Life until Natural Death to Mobile Phone Radiofrequency Field Representative of a 1.8 GHz GSM Base Station Environmental Emission." *Environmental Research* 165: 496–503. doi: 10.1016/j.envres.2018.01.037.

Federal Communications Commission. 2015. "RF Safety FAQ." Last modified November 25, 2015. https://www.fcc.gov/engineering-technology/electromagnetic-compatibility-division/radio-frequency-safety/faq/rf-safety.

Foerster, Milena, Arno Thielens, Wout Joseph, Marloes Eeftens, and Martin Röösli. 2018. "A Prospective Cohort Study of Adolescents' Memory Performance and Individual Brain Dose of Microwave Radiation from Wireless Communication." *Environmental Health Perspectives* 126 (7). doi: 10.1289/EHP2427.

Gandhi, Gursatej, Gurpreet Kaur, and Uzma Nisar. 2015. "A Cross-Sectional Case Control Study on Genetic Damage in Individuals Residing in the Vicinity of a Mobile Phone Base Station." *Electromagnetic Biology and Medicine* 34 (4): 344–54. doi: 10.3109/15368378.2014.933349.

Glaser, Zorach. 1972. "Bibliography of Reported Biological Phenomena ("Effects") and Clinical Manifestations Attributed to Microwave and Radio-Frequency Radiation." *US Naval Medical Research Institute* Research Report MF12.524.015-0004B. Report Number 2.

Golomb, Beatrice A. 2018. "Diplomats' Mystery Illness and Pulsed Radiofrequency/Microwave Radiation." *Neural Computation* 30 (11): 2882–985. doi: 10.1162/neco_a_01133.

Goodreads. 2018. "Robert O. Becker." Quotes. Last accessed November 25, 2018. https://www.goodreads.com/author/quotes/376294.Robert_O_Becker.

Gorpinchenko, Igor, Oleg Nikitin, Oleg Banyra, and Alexander Shulyak. 2014. "The Influence of Direct Mobile Phone Radiation on Sperm Quality." *Central European Journal of Urology* 67: 65–71. doi: 10.5173/ceju.2014.01.art14.

Havas, Magada. 2018. "The Electromagnetic Spectrum–Simplified." Dr. Magda Havas, PhD. Accessed November 16, 2018. http://magdahavas.com/.

Hawkin, Abe. 2018. "Mobile Phone Firms Warning Shareholders about Potential Health Risks of Radio Signals—But Don't Tell Customers." *The Sun*, June 2nd 2018. https://www.thesun.co.uk/tech/6438283/mobile-phone-radio-signal-cancer-warnings/.

Ibitayo, A.O., O. B. Afolabi, A. J. Akinyemi, T. I. Ojiezeh, K. O. Adekoya, and O. O. Ojewunmi. 2017. "RAPD Profiling, DNA Fragmentation, and Histomorphometric Examination in Brains of Wistar Rats Exposed to Indoor 2.5 Ghz Wi-Fi Devices Radiation." *BioMed Research International* vol. 2017, Article ID 8653286, 6 pages. doi: 10.1155/2017/8653286.

Klinghardt, Dietrich. 2012. "Smart Meters & EMR: The Health Crisis of Our Time." YouTube video, 43:11. September 27, 2012. https://www.youtube.com/watch?v=b_wxM6IAF1I.

Kumar, Neelima R., Sonika Sangwan, and Pooja Badotra. 2011. "Exposure to Cell Phone Radiations Produces Biochemical Changes in Worker Honey Bees." *Toxicology International* 18 (1): 70–2. doi: 10.4103/0971-6580.75869.

Leszczynski, Dariusz. 2017. "Current Safety Limits for Cell Phones Do Not Protect All Users." *Between a Rock and a Hard Place* (blog), October 19, 2017. https://betweenrockandhardplace.wordpress.com/2017/05/24/current-safety-limits-for-cell-phones-do-not-protect-all-users-human-health-safety-vs-compliance-with-safety-limits/.

Masoumi, Ali, Narges Karbalaei, S. M. J. Mortazavi, and Mohammad Shabani. 2018. "Radiofrequency Radiation Emitted from Wi-Fi (2.4 GHz) Causes Impaired Insulin Secretion and Increased Oxidative Stress in Rat Pancreatic Islets." *International Journal of Radiation Biology* 94 (9): 1–20. doi: 10.1080/09553002.2018.1490039.

Mohammad, Seyed, Javad Mortazavi, Maryam Paknahad, Iman Khaleghi, and Masha Eghlidospour. 2018. "Effect of Radiofrequency Electromagnetic Fields (RF-EMFS) from Mobile Phones on Nickel Release from Orthodontic Brackets: An In Vitro Study." *International Orthodontics* 16 (3): 562–70. doi: 10.1016/j.ortho.2018.06.013.

Moskowitz, Joel M. 2018. "National Toxicology Program Finds Cell Phone Radiation Causes Cancer." Electromagnetic Radiation Safety. Last modified October 24, 2018. https://www.saferemr.com/2016/05/national-toxicology-progam-finds-cell.html.

Pall, Martin L. 2013. "Electromagnetic Fields Act via Activation of Voltage-Gated Calcium Channels to Produce Beneficial or Adverse Effects." *Journal of Cellular and Molecular Medicine* 17 (8): 958–65. doi: 10.1111/jcmm.12088.

———. 2018. "5G: Great risk for EU, US and International Health! Compelling Evidence for Eight Distinct Types of Great Harm Caused by Electromagnetic Field (EMF) Exposures and the Mechanism that Causes Them." https://peaceinspace.blogs.com/files/5g-emf-hazards--dr-martin-l.-pall--eu-emf2018-6-11us3.pdf.

Pandey, Neelam, Sarbani Giri, Samrat Das, and Puja Upadhaya. 2017. "Radiofrequency Radiation (900 MHz)-Induced DNA Damage and Cell Cycle Arrest in Testicular Germ Cells in Swiss Albino Mice." *Toxicology and Industrial Health* 33 (4): 373–84. doi: 10.1177/0748233716671206.

Parents for Safe Technology. n.d. "Worldwide Precautionary Action." Last accessed November 16, 2018. http://www.parentsforsafetechnology.org/worldwide-countries-taking-action.html.

Petitdant, Nicolas, Anthony Lecomte, Franck Robidel, Christelle Gamez, Kelly Blazy, and Anne-Sophie Villégier. 2018. "Alteration of Adaptive Behaviors of Progeny after Maternal Mobile Phone Exposure. *Environmental Science and Pollution Research* 25 (11): 10894–903. doi: 10.1007/s11356-017-1178-5.

Sangün, Ö, B. Dündar, S. Çömlekçi, and A. Büyükgebiz. 2015. "The Effects of Electromagnetic Field on the Endocrine System in Children and Adolescents." *Pediatric Endocrinology Reviews* 13 (2): 531–45.

Saravanamuttu, Sivani, A. Jayakumar, V. Rebecca, V. Amirtha, and Sudarsanam Dorairaj. 2016. "Survey of People Living at the Vicinity of Cellular Base Transmitting Stations in an Urgan and a Rural Locality." *International Journal of Current Research* 8 (3): 28186–193. https://www.researchgate.net/publication/301677652.

Schoeni Anna, Katharina Roser, and Martin Röösli. 2015. "Memory Performance, Wireless Communication and Exposure to Radiofrequency Electromagnetic Fields: A Prospective Cohort Study in Adolescents." *Environmental International* 85 (2015): 343–51. doi: 10.1016/j.envint.2015.09.025.

Sharma, V. P. and Neelima R. Kumar. 2010. "Changes in Honey Bee Behaviour and Biology under the Influence of Cell Phone Radiations." *Current Science* 98 (10): 1376–78. https://www.researchgate.net/publication/2251877 45_Changes_in_honey_bee_behaviour_and_biology_ under_the_influence_of_cell_phone_radiations.

Sirav, Bahriye and Nesrin Seyhan. 2011. "Effects of Radiofrequency Radiation Exposure on Blood-Brain Barrier Permeability in Male and Female Rats."

Electromagnetic Biology and Medicine 30 (4): 253–60. doi: 10.3109/15368378.2011.600167.

Sun, Yulong, Lin Zong, Zhen Gao, Shunxing Zhu, Jian Tong, and Yi Cao. 2017. "Mitochondrial DNA Damage and Oxidative Damage in HL-60 Cells Exposed to 900MHz Radiofrequency Fields." *Mutation Research* 797–99 (March): 7–14. doi: 10.1016/j.mrfmmm.2017.03.001.

The Baby Safe Project. 2017. "The Joint Statement on Pregnancy and Wireless Radiation." BabySafeProject.org.

Vitelli, Romeo. 2017. "Does Your Child Have a Digital Addiction?" *Psychology Today*, November 23, 2017. https://www.psychologytoday.com/us/blog/media-spotlight/201711/does-your-child-have-digital-addiction.

Wall, Stephen, Zhong-Min Wang, Thomas Kendig, Dina Dobraca, and Michael Lipsett. 2018. "Real-world Cellular Phone Radiofrequency Electromagnetic Field Exposures." *Environmental Research*. Available online October 3, 2018. doi: 10.1016/j.envres.2018.09.015.

Wu, Ting, Theodore S. Rappaport, and Christopher M. Collins. 2015. "Safe for Generations to Come: Considerations of Safety for Millimeter Waves in Wireless Communications." *IEEE Microwave Magazine* 16 (2): 65–84. doi: 10.1109/MMM.2014.2377587.

ABOUT THE AUTHORS

Susan Jeffrey Busen

Susan is an award-winning bestselling author, an investigative health coach, and an international speaker who helps find resolution for people and animals who are struggling with physical or emotional distress. Susan is a former environmental biologist and research scientist whose own health challenges led her to explore natural health, healing, and numerous holistic modalities. She is an avid researcher, an advocate of health freedom and environmental awareness, and a non-GMO activist. Susan is the founder of GetSet™ Tapping, which includes EFT, and the founder of Tap into Balance and My Pet Healer.

Susan's passion is helping people overcome life's traumas, release negative emotions, achieve balance, and come to a place of peace in their lives.

After suffering a debilitating illness and realizing that she was being injured by common technology, she has devoted her life to telling her story, bringing awareness to the issue, and doing what she can to create change. She struggles to survive in "civilization" and spends as much time as possible off the grid. She is the author of 10 books and the mother of three amazing sons.

Tom Busen

Tom graduated from Kendall College with a degree in hospitality management. He is an event coordinator and LOA practitioner. He enjoys organizing events to raise funds for charities.

Will Busen

Will graduated from DePaul University with a degree in finance. He is an author, world traveler, fitness guru, aspiring entrepreneur, and life enthusiast. He spends most of his time in Chicago, Illinois and Austin, Texas.

Dan Busen

Dan recently graduated from DePaul University with a degree in marketing. In his free time, he enjoys weight lifting, biking, and traveling.

51335926R10122

Made in the USA
Columbia, SC
20 February 2019